Prescribing
Learning

A guide to good practice in learning and health

Kathryn James

NIACE
THE NATIONAL ORGANISATION
FOR ADULT LEARNING

Published by the National Institute of
Adult Continuing Education (England and Wales)
21 De Montfort Street
Leicester LE1 7GE

Company registration no. 2603322
Charity registration no. 1002775

ISBN 1 86201 135 4

First published 2001

NIACE, the national organisation for adult learning, has a broad remit to
promote lifelong learning opportunities for adults. NIACE works to develop
increased participation in education and training, particularly for those who
do not have easy access because of barriers of class, gender, age, race, language
and culture, learning difficulties and disabilities, or insufficient financial
resources.

NIACE's website is found at www.niace.org.uk

Cataloguing in Publications Data
A CIP record for this title is available from the British Library

Designed and typeset by Boldface, London EC1
Printed and bound in Great Britain by Alden Press

Contents

Acknowledgements

This publication would not have been possible without the help, support and encouragement of many people.

I would like to thank my colleagues at NIACE: Peter Lavender, Veronica McGivney, Jeannie Sutcliffe and Fiona Aldridge.

I would also like to thank Sue Atkinson, Chris Minter and Malcolm Rigler for their helpful comments and suggestions. Thanks also to Des Conway, Heather Downey and Lesley Hamilton for their information and advice.

Thanks to all the tutors, project workers and learners who shared their practice and experience with me, which provided a wealth of information and a constant source of inspiration.

This publication was partly funded by money from the Department for Education and Skills and also the East Midlands Development Agency and the Nottingham Health Action Zone. We would like to thank them for their support.

Introduction

Good health and poor health are often a matter of personal perception. Feeling discontented and unhappy with life may lead people to dwell on physical feelings of ill-health, just as people who are fully engaged with life may brush off physical symptoms with retorts like 'I'm too busy to be ill'. Both perceptions of health are real for the individual, and are reflections of the wider context of an individual's lived experience, of a sense of community, social interaction and social inclusion, within which sit our personal perceptions of health.

Health is no longer seen as a narrowly defined medical issue. Healthcare professionals are encouraged to recognise the wider socio-economic determinants of health, such as education, unemployment and income. Participation in adult learning, in its many guises, is also affected by these socio-economic determinants. People who are unemployed, on low incomes, or with few qualifications, are less likely to participate in learning as an adult. Participation in learning can also be a catalyst for socio-economic change, leading to improved employment opportunities, social interaction, or involvement in children's learning. This book shows what can happen when you put learning and health together.

Learning that promotes health improvement is a growing area of work, and one where new approaches are being sought every day. The picture, however, is patchy, with some excellent work that has far-reaching effects and shows evidence of real partnership working and 'joined-up' thinking.

This book is not about the learning of healthcare staff. Whilst the training and continued professional development of healthcare staff is very important and has a bearing on health improvement, it is not within the remit of this book. This book is for practitioners and policy-makers in health improvement and adult learning, who want to develop opportunities that will address the health and learning needs of individuals and communities.

Part 1 sets out some of the policy themes that link widening participation in learning and health improvement. Part 2 attempts to plot the terrain of learning in relation to health and describes some of the innovative work that is being done. It also explores the wider benefits of such work, which can have deep and profound effects on individuals' lives. Part 3 is about the strategies and approaches that contribute to good practice. Part 4 looks to the future, at what needs to happen next in the arena of learning for health improvement.

At NIACE we hope this book will trigger new ideas, and that individuals and organisations will start to talk together, to develop shared approaches in order to redress the inequalities in both education and health.

Part I

Learning and health—
a shared agenda

Chapter 1 explains how socio-economic factors affect the health of individuals and families. It also shows that individual health is an expression of the health of communities, and that communities with high levels of social exclusion and social isolation undermine the health of individuals within that community. Both these factors have an immediate negative effect on an individual's sense of well-being, and on their longer-term health. The chapter argues that learning can have a positive effect on health, but that those who are more likely to experience negative social and economic effects on their health are less likely to be participating in learning.

Linking learning and health is a means of addressing issues of health inequality and non-participation in learning.

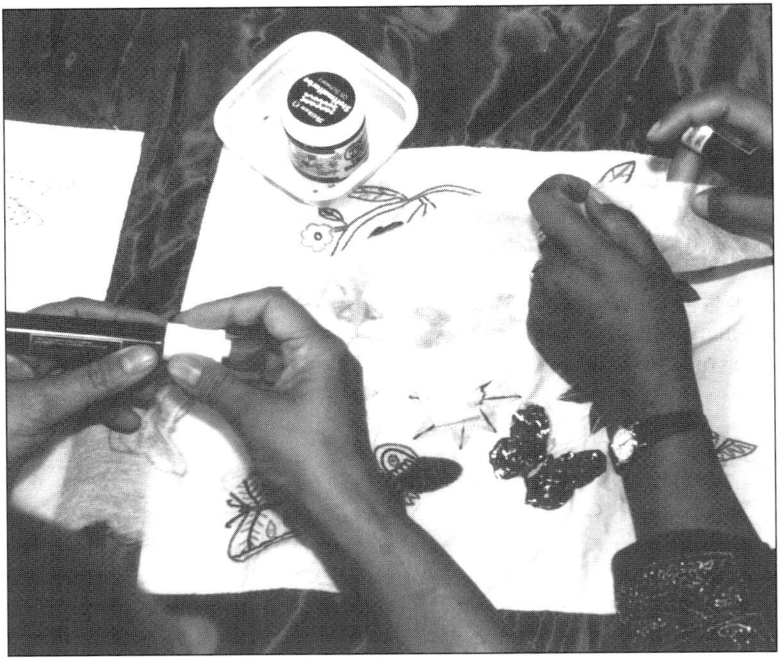

NICK HAYES

Making the case

There is increasing recognition that the different parts of our lives are connected. How we feel about ourselves, how we spend our time and whom we spend it with, what we achieve and what we find rewarding in all areas of our lives have a profound effect on our health and well-being.

As individuals we also have a connection with the communities in which we live, work and learn. Again, feelings of being included and valued, of belonging, and of feeling safe and secure, will affect how we operate and participate in our communities—and how we feel about ourselves as individuals.

There is also a connection between individuals, communities and society in general. Our age, gender, race, culture, income, education, employment, and where we live will all affect how we feel the rest of society perceives us, and how we access services and facilities. These factors will also affect the quality of our lives and how long we live.

Health is a bigger issue than medicine

The World Health Organisation (WHO) defines health, as:

'...a state of complete physical, mental and social well-being, and not merely the absence of disease or infirmity.'

While criticised widely for being too narrow, the WHO

definition does, however, highlight that health is more than the absence of ill health and, therefore, requires more than medical treatment. It also has a positive connotation that health is about the total sense of well-being of an individual. Health, therefore, has many dimensions and is more than just a medical issue.

In 1980 *Inequalities in Health* was published,[1] followed in 1998 by *The Health Divide*.[2] Both these reports revealed that, in the UK, the biggest determinant of health and mortality is social class. In summary, the reports concluded that, in the 1980s, the risks to life for lower occupational classes were much higher than those of the highest occupational classes at every stage. Put bluntly, stillbirths, deaths among babies, children and adolescents, and deaths of working-age adults are higher among people who are poorer. The evidence also shows that the full range of diseases, with very few exceptions, affect the poorer classes more than the rich. Furthermore, people in manual, semi-skilled and unskilled occupations have higher rates of chronic disease and disability than non-manual groups. People in lower socio-economic groups also have poorer fitness scores and register a lack of psychological well-being, evidenced by lack of energy, pain, sleep disturbance, physical immobility, emotional distress and social isolation.

More recent evidence would suggest that very little has changed in the past 20 years. While life expectancy rates have risen across the social spectrum, they have risen unevenly. For example, professional men in social class I can expect to live 9.5 years longer than unskilled manual-working men in social class V.[3]

The Acheson Report[4] also reported on the inequalities in 'healthy life expectancy'—the measure of average length of life free from ill health and disability. In 1996, 17 per cent of men and 25 per cent of women aged 45–64 in social class I reported limiting long-standing illness, in contrast with 48 per cent of men and 45 per cent of women aged 45–64 in social class V.[4] Poorer people will not only die earlier, but they will also spend more years experiencing chronic illness and/or disability. *The Acheson Report* concluded that the socio-economic determinants of health, such as education, employment and income, are as important in determining health as lifestyle factors. The report not only recognised the problems of health inequality, but also sought to find some solutions to the problem. The report recommended that policies to tackle inequalities in health need to be both 'upstream', for example, aimed at raising income levels of individuals and families, and 'downstream', for example, providing support for health-promoting behaviours and activities. The review recommended that policies needed to be cross-departmental, and not just the responsibility of health departments.

Social class involves much more than occupational group; it is also about income, wealth, educational qualifications, and expected life chances. Where you live, what you eat and choices in how you live your life are also inter-related.

Research into stress biology looks at the relationship between chronic stress and the nervous system, the cardiovascular and the immune systems, cholesterol levels, blood pressure, blood clotting, and immunity. Anxiety, insecurity, low self-esteem, social isolation, and lack of control over life and work can trigger a biological stress-response. If this response is triggered too often and for too long, evidence suggests that there may be multiple health implications, including depression, susceptibility to infection, diabetes, high blood pressure, and accumulation of cholesterol in blood vessel walls, with increased risks of heart attack and stroke.[5]

There is also a 'double whammy' effect. Factors like poor housing, having nowhere safe for your children to run about and play, worry about paying bills, and having no one to turn to when you have a problem, will affect your sense of mental well-being and physical health in the short-term. The effect of such anxieties will also have a longer-term negative impact on people's health. A woman who is participating in the Nottingham 'Prescriptions for Learning' project had this to say when asked about her health and quality of life:

'There is so much in this life that puts you down, gets you down, it's hard to think of anything good.'

A respondent, quoted in a mental health survey, revealed how people have to forego basic items, such as good quality food, decent clothes, social life and holidays:[6]

'Because of my low income…I go for foods with cheaper prices and those with special offers, I have not bought any new clothes for years and have not been out for a meal, cinema or a holiday for more than 10 years.'

Another respondent said:

'All in all I find the experience of being on low income degrading.'

The impact of low income on individual's sense of well-being is evident. However, ill health is also more than the problems that individuals experience. A person may have a decent income and education, and may not indulge in risk-taking behaviours, but may still experience poor health and well-being because there is also a social and cultural context to health. The sense of health and well-being that many individuals experience is not a problem or a deficit within themselves, but actually a reflection or a response to the situation they find themselves in. Wilkinson points to a number of studies that show the beneficial health effects of more social contact between people at home and in the community.[7]

Imagine a mother at home with a baby, unless she has opportunities to meet with other parents, or time to call her own, she will be vulnerable to feeling lonely, bored or irritable. Imagine also somebody who is unemployed and lives in a ' commuter village', where the last shop has closed and the bus service doesn't run anymore. They are also likely to feel isolated, cut-off from social contact and discouraged. Such individuals may eventually end up at the doctor's surgery with anxiety, stress or depression. They are probably quite physically healthy people, but their sense of well-being has been compromised. The symptoms they are experiencing are actually the symptoms of ill-health arising from loss of community, social exclusion, and the loss of social capital.

The connection between society and the communities we live in has such a profound effect on individuals that it affects their sense of well-being. If we undermine an individual's sense of well-being, the long-term effects of living with that level of stress will manifest itself in physical ill-health.

Saving lives—a Government policy

The Government White Paper *Saving Lives: Our Healthier Nation* is based on the belief that poor health can be attributable to social, economic and environmental factors and that

> 'individuals can make decisions about their and their families' health which can make a difference.'[8]

The Government recognises that there are inequalities in health, just as there are in education and housing, and that there is a link between many of the factors that contribute to poor health: poverty, low wages, unemployment, poor initial education, crime and fear of crime, and a polluted environment.

The White Paper stresses the importance of education in particular:

> 'Education is vital to health. People with low levels of educational achievement are more likely to have poor health as adults … By improving education for all we will tackle one of the main causes of inequality in health.' [8]

The Acheson Report in 1998 also highlighted the role of education as an important determinant in health inequality. Level of education, it stated, has an important role in influencing inequalities in socio-economic position, as educational qualifications determine an individual's labour-market position:

> 'As a consequence, education is a traditional route out of poverty for those living in disadvantage.'[4]

Multi-disciplinary and cross-sectoral partnership working is seen as the key to addressing the wider determinants of health (including education and social inclusion), and as a way of tackling particular aspects of ill-health (such as coronary heart disease, cancer, mental health, and accidents). *The Saving Lives White Paper* has required Health Authorities to develop and implement health improvement plans (HImPs), to address local health and social problems, and health inequalities. Health Authorities are expected to involve local stakeholders in carrying these plans forward. In 2000, the NHS Plan further strengthened the policy emphasis on tackling inequality by including the development of local strategic partnerships, to forge greater links between health, education, employment and other causes of social exclusion. The need for, and the opportunities for, multi-sectoral partnership working have never been greater.

Impact of learning on health

Research into the impact of learning on health has been carried out by NIACE. Four hundred and seventy-three adults and 47 groups completed a questionnaire about the general benefits of learning, and the impact learning had on their physical and mental health.[9] Eighty-seven per cent of respondents reported benefits to their physical health, citing feeling less ill, managing pain more effectively, and feeling less tired. Also quoted were improvements to family health, better health behaviours and psychological well-being. Eighty-nine per cent of respondents experienced positive emotional or mental health benefits, such as 'feeling mentally better', changed health behaviours, distraction from dwelling on ill-health or poor circumstances, and psychological displacement activity helping them to deal with pain, such as bereavement.

Individuals reported positive benefits such as:

'I sleep better, feel happier, etc. The feelings of self-worth, confidence and realisation of dreams have all contributed to a very positive and sustainable manner.'

'I don't take tablets any more and do not suffer from depression. Since my mental and emotional state has improved, so has my physical health.'

The findings of the report indicate that returning to learning does make people feel better. The reasons for this are many and varied. It may be that returning to learning gives individuals a reason to get out of the house, and being physically more active may promote better sleeping. Returning to learning is an opportunity to make new friends and be more socially active. It can also be about the realisation of potential, the affirmation of skills and abilities, and a feeling of going somewhere in life.[10]

As we have seen, learning is a traditional route out of poverty. If returning to learning has such a positive impact on people's sense of well-being, why then do some people choose not to participate in learning?[11]

Betty is a woman in her 50's, has significant health difficulties and lives with her husband Barry who has multiple scler-osis. She illustrated how learning can have many positive outcomes:

'My husband and I are carers for each other. He looks after me because of my physical difficulties and I look after him because of his mental health difficulties. He gets depressed and his memory keeps going. We also have a disabled child, who we care for; we also look in on an old lady in our street and seem to get called on by other people to help out. We got involved with learning because our doctor recommended it. I think he thought it would improve the quality of our lives. So far we have done art and craft type things like glass painting and Barry does watercolour painting, which he has discovered a talent for.

We also got involved with a project called City-net to construct a web site of local information. That was the best thing. The tutor asked us to choose images and music to go on the web site, images that we felt portrayed how we see ourselves. I chose a picture of an old lady who was being comforted by a carer. The carer was sitting next to the old lady talking to her and stroking her hand. I realised that everybody saw me as the carer, but I saw myself as the old lady who needed and wanted to be cared for. I suddenly realised that I don't get enough of that in my life. It was a revelation. It really made me think about things and I learnt a lot about myself just from that one picture.

Learning is a good way for me to care for myself, to get a bit more balance in my life, because it is time for me. I have fun, and have something to look forward to. I also get a chance to put something back. Last Christmas, we taught some of the local children to paint glass candleholders, so they could give them to their mums and dads as presents. This year I think we might help them make Christmas cards.

I am in pain 24 hours a day. Illness for me is like being in a dark room, but getting involved with learning is like having a window in that room that lets light in. My pain will never go away, but learning helps me to cope with it better.'

The story that Betty tells illustrates clearly how a person's learning and their health is connected. For Betty, learning has increased her social contacts, she finds pleasure in her learning and it provides 'light' into her life that enables her to deal with the stress and discomfort of constant pain. It has also given Betty an understanding of the 'economics of relationships', that receiving love and support is as necessary as giving love and support to other human beings.[7] Betty realised that, in her role as a carer, she needed to have support in order to maintain a sense of well-being.

The learning divide

Many people do not access learning because of the barriers they experience. Barriers to learning can be external, or structural such as:

▶ cost;
▶ unavailability of affordable childcare;
▶ times of courses do not fit in with shift work, or childcare responsibilities;
▶ unavailability of transport, or lack of community-based provision;
▶ buildings not accessible to people with restricted mobility;
▶ marketing of provision only targets certain sections of the community, for example publicity is not provided in community languages, or only depicts images of young people;
▶ insufficient support available to people with learning-support needs;
▶ inappropriate curricula that do not meet the needs of individuals or communities.

Barriers to learning can also be internal or cultural, such as:

▶ previous bad experience of education;
▶ low self-esteem, or lack of confidence in ability;
▶ peer pressure, or if education is not the norm within ones family or community.

Internal or cultural barriers can be very overwhelming, and may be a much greater deterrent to accessing learning than external or structural barriers.

In 1999 NIACE conducted a survey of 5054 adults about their participation in learning. Learning is a very broad term and can mean many things to different people. For the purpose of the survey, learning was defined as:

'practising, studying, or reading about something. It can also mean being taught, instructed or coached. This is so you can develop skills, knowledge, abilities or understanding of something. You can do it regularly (each day or month) or you can do it for a short period of time. It can be full-time or part-time, done at home, at work or in another place, like college. Learning does not have to lead to a qualification.'[11]

The 1999 survey confirmed the findings of previous surveys by showing that there is an adult-learning divide. Age, class, and experience of initial education affect access to learning and the confidence to participate in learning.

Half (50 per cent) of all upper-class and middle-class respondents to the survey were current or recent learners, compared with just over one-third (36 per cent) of the skilled working-class, and nearly one-quarter (24 per cent) of the unskilled working-class and people on limited incomes.[10] Those in work, or seeking work, are twice as likely to be participating in learning as those not working or who are retired.

Length of initial education is another indicator of participation in adult learning. Those who left school at age 16 or earlier had participation rates of 25 per cent, compared with participation rates of 61 per cent among those who stayed on in education post-age 20. (*ibid.*)

The survey revealed other inequalities:

▶ people with access to the Internet were twice as likely to be learning as people without;[12]
▶ people in managerial or professional employment were more likely than their colleagues in non-managerial or unskilled roles to be offered training and staff development at work.

In conclusion, people with fewer qualifications, those in less skilled work and older people tend to be the groups who do not participate in learning.

Information, advice and guidance

In an age where knowledge and skills are key commodities in the labour market, access to information, advice and guidance about learning opportunities is crucial. Yet a recent MORI survey of demand for information, advice and guidance still shows a socio-economic divide in access to services.[13] People who are unemployed or disabled, and those over age 45 express the greatest difficulties in accessing information, advice and guidance—and the greatest dissatisfaction with the services and their outcomes. Thus, too many people are still burdened by the triple disadvantage of being at the wrong end of the health divide, the learning divide, and the guidance divide.

Government policy places a high importance on lifelong learning for all, and widening participation in learning. Yet surveys reveal those at risk of poor health are the groups who do not participate in learning, and that poor health, disability and low self-esteem are still very significant barriers to learning for some people, particularly among some groups.[11,13] It could be argued that participation in learning could have both preventative and health-improving dimensions. As we will see in later chapters, where learning providers work in partnership with health providers there are benefits for both services. Health providers are able to realise health improvements for their patients, and learning providers are able to reach those groups of people who find it hard to access learning, because of poor health, disability, or low self-esteem, and thereby widen participation in learning. One could argue that the cumulative effects of merging the two agendas of health improvement and widening participation in learning could have enormous significance over a longer time for individuals, families and communities.

What do we mean by learning and health?

'Learning and health' is used here as a catch-all phrase for an activity that either involves learning about health, and/or has health improvement as an outcome. Approaches to learning and health include:

▶ learning about health, for example through health-improvement programmes. This can involve giving information on health matters, so that individuals make informed choices about behaviour or lifestyle that will promote good health or prevent ill health, or it may involve addressing community health needs;

▶ learning that occurs through involvement in an activity for a specific health purpose and outcome, usually physical, such as 'Exercise on Prescription';

▶ learning that occurs through involvement in an activity that allows individuals to explore and express feelings, to express creative potential, and to promote a positive sense of mental well-being, such as 'Arts on Prescription';

▶ learning for a more general health outcome that enables individuals to explore how they feel about themselves, and which could impact on behaviour and lifestyle, such as self-esteem raising or assertiveness;

▶ learning whatever an individual is interested in, or wants to achieve, which, where this is a positive experience, has physical or mental health impacts, such as 'Prescriptions for Learning'.

The common feature of all of these is that learning is the activity or medium that generates a positive health outcome. An individual will have learnt something that will have had an improving effect on their health.

Putting approaches to learning and health work in a framework is perhaps a simplistic way to try and place some of the exciting, imaginative and innovative work that is happening, which exists on the margins of healthcare provision and educational provision. This is a kind of 'no-man's land', where the interconnections between health and learning can be very powerful indeed. Here it is possible to explore the real wider benefits of learning. Many of the examples of good practice highlighted in this book are reaching out, and involving, some of the hardest-to-reach individuals and communities in our society, and engaging them in a dialogue about their health and learning needs, which is dynamic and empowering. If we are prepared to listen, this ought to change the way we think about services, and how we have often failed to meet needs.

References

1 Black, D., and Great Britain Working Group on Inequalities in Health. (1980). *Inequalities in Health*, Department of Health and Social Security.

2 Black, D., Townsend, P., Davidson, N., Whitehead, M. and Great Britain Working Group on Inequalities in Health (1992). *Inequalities in Health: The Black Report: The Health Divide*, Penguin Books.

3 Mitchell, R., Dorling, D., Shaw, M. and Joseph Rowntree Foundation (2000). *Inequalities in Life and Death: What if Britain Were More Equal?*, Policy Press.

4 Royal College of General Practitioners (1998). *Independent Inquiry into Inequalities in Health Report (The Acheson Report)*, Royal College of General Practitioners.

5 Mentality (2000). *Making It Happen—A Guide to Delivering Mental Health Promotion*.

6 Bird, L., (August 2001). *'A Life in the Day' Poverty, Social Exclusion and Mental Health: A Survey of People's Personal Experience*, 5:3 Pavilion Press.

7 Wilkinson, R.G. (1996). *Unhealthy Societies: The Afflictions of Inequality*, Routledge.

8 Great Britain Department of Health (1999). *Saving Lives: Our Healthier Nation*, Stationery Office.

9 Aldridge, F., Lavender, P. (1999). *Impact of Learning on Health*, NIACE.

10 Aldridge, F., Tuckett, A. (2001). *Winners and Losers in an Expanding System: The NIACE survey on Adult Participation in Learning 2000*, NIACE.

11 Sargant, N. (2000). *The Learning Divide Revised*, NIACE .

12 Research study conducted by MORI for the Guidance Council (2001) *Demand for Information, Advice and Guidance*.

13 Dench, S., Regan, J., and Great Britain Department for Education and Employment (1999). *Learning in Later Life: Motivation and Impact*, Department of Education and Employment.

Part 2

Approaches to widening participation and improving health

Chapter 2 argues that we need to take a learning approach to health improvement by creating learning environments within health settings, or by taking learning to places where people go. It also suggests that learning about health can give people a shared sense of what is important for their communities, and that addressing the needs of communities can also improve health for individuals and families.

Chapter 3 is about the benefits to physical and mental health that can be achieved through participation in exercise. It also shows how participation in exercise can be an opportunity for learning and social interaction, and that the benefits are the greatest for those with the poorest health.

Hospitals and healthcare settings have begun to commission works of art to add colour, interest and a more uplifting atmosphere to their buildings. However, using the arts as a means of addressing health inequality and promoting inclusion and lifelong learning is a newer concept that is gaining greater momentum. Chapter 4 explores the link between arts, health and learning, and suggests that the benefits include personal learning about self and others, communal learning, increased social interaction, increased use of social facilities and learning about health.

Chapter 5 looks at the role that self-esteem of individuals and communities can play in the reduction of health inequalities and in bridging the learning divide. Most of the initiatives highlighted in this book have sought to raise the self-esteem of individuals by engaging people in activities. In most projects and initiatives raised self-esteem has been regarded as a desirable outcome that results from health improvement, or participation in learning and social interaction. This chapter refers to initiatives that have directly undertaken to tackle the issue of self-esteem and, by doing so, encourage participation in other activities that will promote good health and learning.

The effect learning has on health is considered in Chapter 6. It looks at the key role guidance has on engaging hard-to-reach learners in their learning, and how guidance can be a learning process that has health benefits in itself. This chapter also shows that when healthcare staff are more aware of the learning needs of individuals, it can improve access to healthcare.

Walsall Community Arts 'Mens' Health' Project

2

Learning in
healthcare settings

Healthcare staff increasingly see themselves as health educators. Education about health is recognised as being an important part of the health treatment that healthcare staff offer. Yet to carry out this role, many healthcare staff have to see themselves in a different light and sometimes have to learn new skills. Dr Malcolm Rigler, who transformed the Withymoor Village Surgery into a 'Health Hive' where good communication about health needs was paramount, has written:

> 'Doctors then and now, learned to speak a foreign language—the language of medicine. The only small condescension made towards informing patients was done in a sort of medical baby talk...your waterworks...your ticker...down there.'

Such ways of communicating make the process of understanding and learning very haphazard, and leaves patients dependent and in ignorance. They cannot question, and neither can they make meaningful choices.

All the staff at the Withymoor Surgery realised that if communication was going to take place, then they would have to create an environment in the surgery where people felt free to talk about their health needs. They had many conversations with primary school teachers about how to create a learning environment, where people would be able to ask questions and learn about their health. Just as adult educators pay attention to the learning environment and learning materials, as well as the way tutors facilitate learning, healthcare staff at Withymoor undertook to do the same, in order to achieve a learning environment within the surgery. They looked at the environment that, like many surgeries, was fairly dull, with a few tatty leaflets bending out of racks and a scattering of dog-eared magazines, and created an environment that was more inviting, with fish tanks and plants.

Leaflets were put away, and vibrant messages about health improvement were created by professional artists. Educational toys were made available so that, while people waited or talked to staff, their children could play and learn. They also wanted to encourage parents to play with their children. Artists and writers were invited into the surgery to undertake project work, to create images and text about people's perception of their health, but also to encourage people to creatively express their own thoughts about health. This was an important sharing and learning experience for many people.

Receptionists attended courses provided by the NHS on reception skills, and had many ideas on how to improve the reception areas. Their participation in the arts and health projects led them to join in with some drama, theatre and museum groups. Some of them felt that doing drama enabled them to be better receptionists, in that they were more confident and able to project their voices, and more able to empathise with how patients might be feeling.

Surgeries can be important learning places, and healthcare staff have a crucial role to play as educators. This may involve the development of communication and facilitation skills, to enable them to impart their knowledge. It may also involve partnership with adult educators, as well as artists, poets, writers and other professionals who facilitate communication and expression.

If education has a role in health improvement, then healthcare staff need to think how best they can become educators. This may involve the development of communication and facilitation skills to impart knowledge so that individuals can learn about their health. A learning approach is necessary, as opposed to a teaching, training, or instructional approach. As Dr Rigler stated:

'If we do not recognise that our GP practices can become places of learning for patients and staff alike, then we are missing a golden opportunity.'

Pharmacies can also be important learning places, particularly so in small rural villages, or on housing estates, where shops and other community resources find it increasingly hard to keep going, and where pharmacies are one of the few remaining services left.

Green Light Pharmacy may look like a typical chemist's shop from the outside, but they have taken a learning approach to pharmacy and the prescribing of medicines. The pharmacist is not tucked away at the back, but takes a front-of-house role. There are seating areas, so customers an discuss their diagnosis or health problem with the pharmacist. The pharmacist will take time to listen to the customer and to help them understand why they have developed that particular problem, what the treatment does, and how to use the treatment most effectively. (On average, the pharmacist estimates that he does about 30 consultations per day, some lasting as long as 20 minutes.) Customers can also use a touchscreen to access information on health, diet, medicines, comple mentary therapies etc, and can print off the information to take away and read.

The pharmacy also offers, free of charge, other services, such as measuring blood pressure and cholesterol levels, and testing for diabetes. All testing is done with full explanations and health advice. There is a consulting room when more privacy is required or when other practitioners visit, such as a chiropodist. In the evening, the shop is opened up to people to attend the courses and talks that Green Light Pharmacy puts on about subjects such as diabetes and asthma.

Green Light Pharmacy recently ran a course on asthma for the local Bengali community, run by pharmacists John Foreman and Tim

O'Donoghue, and a nurse. Time was taken to research the cultural issues around asthma for that community, and an interpreter was used who Green Light have already trained in pharmaceutical and medical terminology. Tim O'Donaghue said:

> 'lots of people, even very educated people, can hold myths and wrong assumptions about health that can affect how they take new medication. In our courses we check out what people think about their illnesses, and then work with them to ensure they have a proper understanding of why they might have become ill and what they can do about it, including exercise, diet and lifestyle. As well as how to take their medication. We give information at about first year university physiology level and people seem to be able to understand it.'

Courses attract up to about 20 people at a time, and people do come back for more information. Tim O 'Donoghue said:

> 'Giving people information about their health is very empowering, not just telling them what to do, but why to do it and why it works, is important.'

Learning about health is also about challenging perceptions about our own health and about the health of others. People can have simple misconceptions about health because they have not been fully informed, or because they have not been asked what they think they already know. Tim O'Donoghue illustrated the point that when people do not have their medications explained to them properly, they do not always realise the implications of not taking them correctly:

> 'We find that people with high blood pressure who are on tablets for hypertension will tell us they haven't been taking their medication because they haven't been feeling stressed.'

Approximately 10 per cent of the NHS budget goes on prescribed medicines, and 50 per cent of people do not take their medication correctly, often with catastrophic results. In terms of health economics, 15 minutes of learning about health can save a lot of public money in the end. Green Light Pharmacy is hoping that, by helping people to learn about their illnesses and treatment, they can improve this statistic and, importantly, help people improve their health.

> Lloyds pharmacy has opened up CHAT centres in some of their pharmacies, which are areas dedicated to the provision of informal advice and signposting, using leaflets and specialist events. Many people already use their local pharmacies for information on health needs rather than making an appointment to see their GP, or as a strategy to decide whether to make an appointment or not. Lloyds pharmacy feel there is more that can be done to develop the pharmacy as a community resource, where individuals can learn about their health needs.

Learning about health in community settings

Another approach is to take learning about health to places where people are.

> The 'Add Life' health improvement courses, set up in partnership between Health Promotion, Age Concern, Community Leisure and South Downs NHS Trust, offered four six-week courses to residents of four sheltered housing schemes. Each weekly session of two hours was followed by Extend and relaxation exercise. Topics for the sessions included: healthy eating, taken by the community dietician; keeping independent and preventing accidents and falls, taken by a health promotion advisor; managing medicines safely, taken by a community pharmacist; and Age Concern's Information Centre and Cyber Café.
>
> All learners rated courses as enjoyable and informative, and residents have since requested regular exercise sessions (Extend, Tai Chi,

or line dancing), regular sessions (art or story writing) and hand massage. They have also requested a residents' newsletter, having speakers in, and arranged outings. As one learner on the 'Add Life' course said:

> 'It's great to be treated as if you haven't lost your marbles because you are elderly.'

It seems that introducing learning and health into this setting has actually been a catalyst for residents to recognise their own learning potential, and the pleasure that they can derive from it.

Another good example of effective health education, which involved partnership working and provided learning about health in places where men go, is a project that took place in Walsall.

Walsall's 'Men's Health 2000' project was a Health Action Zone project led by Walsall Community Arts, which sought to address the poor health of men in the east Walsall area. The project worked on the basis that men do not go to the doctor because they are scared, fearful, embarrassed, or do not think it is a manly thing to do. The project, involving health and arts workers, decided to use humour as an antidote to these fears and attitudes. The project also decided to go where men go—to pubs and clubs—and to offer healthcare checks and advice, but also to use artists and a stand-up comedian to encourage the men to talk and explore their own health perceptions. The men were offered height, weight, body mass index and blood pressure testing, and a chance to discuss lifestyle issues, such as diet, exercise, smoking, safe sex and stress. A pair of fake testicles provided much hilarity, but also enabled men to learn how to check for lumps that might be testicular cancer. The men were asked to complete a questionnaire, and their answers and stories formed the basis of a stand-up comedy routine that was performed to a combined audience of approximately 300 people.[1]

The 'Men's Health 2000' project was an innovative way of providing a better take-up of screening services, by taking the service to men. In so doing, it picked up eight men with high blood pressure among the 46 who attended the second round of screening. The project also enabled men to learn about health issues, such as testicular cancer, and to explore their attitudes about their health. As some male participants in the project explained:

> 'Men hold things back for far too long—sometimes until its fatal.'

> 'Men will talk endlessly, when they've had a few, about their broken noses and shattered bones. But anything more personal than that, never!'

The project, through educating and supporting behaviour change, enabled men to consider health improvement:

> 'I don't walk enough, but I'm going to change that.'

> 'I check for breast cancer, even though you usually associate that with women.'

The project also highlighted the immensity of the health improvement work that needed to be done to achieve better health for men in that area. Of the 46 men in the second round of screening, 38 were consuming more than the recommended 28 units of alcohol per week, 14 were taking over 50 units, and five over 100 units. Thirty-eight were smokers, with 30 smoking more than 20 per day. Ten men said they did not eat any fruit and vegetables (except chips). Seventeen men were pre-obese and four were obese. Many of these findings are consistent with national epidemiological data on men's health, but providing such local information has highlighted the issues for the people of Walsall, and pushed men's health towards the top of local health agendas. It has also shown that providing information, advice and support to men on their health in a setting that suits them is feasible, workable and necessary.[1]

It is possible to engage hard-to-reach sections of the community in learning about health if you are prepared to take learning opportunities to them, and to be imaginative in the way that health improvement is delivered.[2]

CEDC (Community Education Development Centre) estimated that over 35,000 young men play weekend football in the West Midlands alone. Despite involvement in sport, many of the young men could still be classified as 'at risk' because of other health behaviours, such as drinking, smoking, unsafe sex, other risk-taking behaviour, and reluctance to use GP services. Finding what motivates and interests people, and working with them in their own environment, was the impetus for the 'Alive and Kicking' project.

> 'Alive and Kicking' was a project led by CEDC (and funded by the Department of Health) that arose from concern over men's health and sought to involve men in health improvement by targeting men's weekend football. The project targeted a lower level league, where players tend to be less fit, and devised tasks for health improvement that were relevant, for example a healthy diet was called a 'Performance Diet'. The teams were given points for participating in tasks, and a health-league table was devised. Winners of the health-league won prizes, such as a new team strip. A key strength of the project was that it used the interests and motivations of the individuals and the teams to learn about healthier lifestyles. Again, we see a learning approach to health by taking learning to learners, and an approach that hooks into learner's motivations. It also provided a blueprint for how the project could have been sustained by partnership between a Community Health Trust, Local Authority and local professional football club.[2]

Learning about health can break down barriers to learning

The work carried out by Thomas Danby College with *Big Issue* vendors also shows that, by tapping into individual and group interests and motivations, you can set up very successful learning provision that can take place in a college environment.[3] Maggi Butterworth, co-ordinator, wrote:

> 'Being homeless and semi-jobless means that the basics most people take for granted, such as hot meals and a reasonable diet, can be out of our reach. People who are malnourished find it difficult enough to get back on their feet, much less in to work. *Big Issue* vendors in Leeds had expressed an interest in learning how to cook healthy meals after discussions with their support worker.'

A course was set up in a community kitchen on Wednesday evenings so that learners could cook and eat together. The course eventually moved to the main campus and, despite initial apprehensions, the learners agreed that they preferred that venue because it offered better facilities. As well as being a step back into learning, it was also an important social occasion for the vendors, who don't often get the chance to meet up with each other. One group member said:

> 'We have learned basic cooking skills and can prepare healthy, tasty and cheap meals. We are learning basics of nutrition and what makes up a healthy diet.'

Group members have also gained certificates in food safety and emergency first aid, and how to use a digital camera and scanner. Other learning opportunities are regularly explored, usually when everyone is sitting around the table after their meal.

Another learner said:

> 'Going back into education is the best thing for anybody to do if they want to improve their lives.'

Greg is 27 years old and a graduate in information technology. His story shows how learning addressed some of his immediate health needs, but also how it opened his eyes to other possibilities in his life. Greg lost his job in computing because his increasing use of drugs seriously affected his time-keeping. Greg found himself on the streets, but last year he became a *Big Issue* vendor. Now things have started to improve as a result of joining in with the 'Big Bites for *Big Issue* Vendors' course in cooking cheap and healthy meals. Finding employment is difficult, despite his degree, as Greg still does not have somewhere permanent to live and his skills in computing are already out of date. Taking a positive step, by doing the course at Thomas Danby College, has given Greg some hope. He anticipates being a vendor for another year, but has definite plans to move on.

'It has made me think about updating my computer skills. It has been a great success.'

Addressing the fundamental health needs of individuals through learning can be the impetus for them to consider other aspects of their lives that they may wish to change. Providing learning within an educational setting means that some of the barriers to participating in learning have already been broken down, making progression onto further learning opportunities an easier step to take.[4]

A community approach to health

One approach to health improvement is to look at the way the social structures and resources of a local community are affecting the health of individuals. Social support and social contact are now generally accepted as having an important beneficial effect on health.

'Lack of a confiding relationship with a close friend, relative or partner is associated with poorer health, but so also is less involvement with wider social networks, community activities, etc'.[4]

One of the ways to improve health, therefore, is to improve the opportunities people have for social contact and for social support. However, in order to see what social structures communities need, it might be necessary to first find out what social contact and social support individuals lack.

Health visitors play an important role in learning and health, because they visit people in their homes, and get a real sense of families and communities. They can collect the 'health stories' of individuals, which, in turn, create a bigger picture of the health needs of a community. For example, with their particular responsibility towards young children and their preparation for schooling, a health visitor may see that the development of individual children is suffering because parents do not have a local playgroup, or nursery. In this case the local health-needs assessment for that community involves the need for improved learning and play opportunities for its young children, and opportunities for parents to meet, thereby increasing their social contact and support.

Given that a major source of stress in most peoples lives is caused and exacerbated by low income, and that increased social networks have an improving effect on health, the community approach to health taken by the LETS scheme (Local Exchange Trading System) set up on the Earlsfield estate is likely to be profound. The aim of the project is to bring the community together, introducing ways for them to save money, and developing a social network by setting up a LETS scheme, whereby residents swap skills, goods and services. The project has been set up by the Earlesfield Community Forum, funded by the Adult and Community Learning Fund, and in partnership with Grantham College, Mid-Kesteven Primary Care Group, and the local District Council. The directory of skills shows an impressive list, from baby-sitting and childcare, carpentry, plumbing and electrical skills, computing skills, a listening ear, knitting baby clothes, ironing, shopping, baking, blackberry picking, gardening, hairdressing, dog walking and many more.

The list also shows the raised level of interaction that results from the scheme, and the building of new support networks. One woman, who was new to the area and lived by herself, described the new support network she had:

> 'After I came out of hospital it was really good because, for the first couple of weeks, I was a bit of a crock, and one lady did some ironing for me. There was someone who could provide transport, even just to the doctors.'

The impressive list surely indicates the breadth of skills within a community, skills that could otherwise remain hidden and unacknowledged. It is also indicative of a developing awareness that individuals within the community had about their levels of skills. As one member said:

> 'A lot of people say "Oh, I can't join 'cos I can't do anything", and initially that was my thought... And then HP came (LETS Co-ordinator) with somebody, and sat down and said "Who did them painted walls?", "You know", I said, "I did". "Oh, put her down for stencilling!"... So, before I knew it, she was off with this list of things I could do. Yeah, it makes you feel... when she was gone, I was thinking, yeah, I can do lots of things.'

As well as setting up a system for swapping skills, goods and services, it also offers free learning programmes and crèche facilities to its members. Courses have been determined by the members and have included: information technology, home maintenance, assert yourself, be bold, be confident, clothing alterations, sewing for a family, and creating a CV. Many of the ideas for courses come from members, arising from their experience of using the trading systems they were setting up on the estate, for example, a thrift rail was the impetus for the clothing alterations course. Evidence of residents' commitment to learning shows in the fact that all courses are fully booked.

The learning outcomes have been numerous. Some learners have achieved qualifications, but there is also much informal learning. For example, the coffee bar has provided learning opportunities by default.

The craft talents of some members have been shared while they attend the coffee bar. Making Christmas cards, plaster models and candles have been popular. The social occasion of this learning has enabled friendships to develop, which, no doubt, have been cemented with the exchange of cards or gifts. A weekly on-site careers advisor is also enabling people to start thinking about training needs and future aspirations.

This project did not seek to address health improvement by engaging people in directly learning about health, but it has nevertheless been a catalyst for learning about health. Creating a social network has meant that people feel less isolated, and have therefore felt more able to come forward with health issues that they wish to discuss and for which they want support. These have included weight loss, head lice, smoking cessation and domestic violence.

As well as this increased interest in health matters, one health visitor reported improvements in assertiveness, communication and personal appearance. The overall health of the community has been improved, by increased social support, social networks and learning opportunities.

Summary

This chapter shows that, to enable people to make decisions about their health and adopt better health behaviours, it is necessary to take a learning approach. Attention needs to be given to the learning environment and learning materials, and to providing learning in community venues. The chapter also provides examples, which illustrate that addressing the learning needs of communities can also be an approach to community health needs.

References

1   Walsall Community Arts (2000). *Walsall Male Art. The Walsall Experience of the Arts in Men's Health*, Experience of Arts in Men's Health, Leisure Services Civic Centre.
2   CEDC (2001). *Alive and Kicking, A Guide to Working with Local Football Teams to Improve Men's Health*, CEDC.
3   Butterworth M. (September 2001). *AoC Beacon Award Proposal*, Thomas Danby College, unpublished.
4   Wilkinson, R.G. (1996). *Unhealthy Societies: The Afflictions of Inequality*, Routledge.

Keighley Healthy Living Centre 'Gardening and Allotment Project'

3

Health and learning through exercise

Exercise is good for your physical health

The link between levels of activity and improved health is well documented.[1] Increased physical activity of moderate intensity is associated with decreased mortality rates, decreased risks of mortality from cardiovascular disease, colon cancer, or later-life onset diabetes. Regular physical activity also prevents or delays the development of hypertension, and reduces blood pressure. It is also important in the prevention of osteoporosis. Physical activity also promotes positive mental health, and relieves symptoms of depression and anxiety.[2] Given that these are all such common illnesses, the promotion of regular physical exercise is important for the prevention of, and recuperation from ill-health. Schemes to support individuals in access to leisure and sporting facilities, or to include physical activity into their everyday lives have increased. Such schemes have given people a clearer understanding of how and why physical activity is good for their health. Individuals have, through the support offered by these schemes, learned how to exercise safely and for improved health. Consideration could be given as to whether such schemes, which maintain physical health and prevent ill-health, should be available to the general public as a major health improvement strategy, or whether they continue to target high-risk groups, such as those with high blood pressure.

For several years, GPs in some parts of the country have been able to refer people at risk of coronary heart disease, or with high blood pressure, to managed exercise programmes such as 'Exercise on Prescription'.

> In 1990 Stockport Borough Council developed one of the first 'Exercise on Prescription' schemes, in response to the high levels of coronary heart disease in parts of Stockport. GPs who participated in the scheme can refer individuals particularly at risk of coronary heart disease to a community health and fitness officer. Individuals are then assessed and guided to the most appropriate physical activity, for the same price as a prescription. All individuals are followed up after ten weeks so their progress can be monitored.
>
> An evaluation of the scheme conducted in 1994 showed that after a ten-week exercise course, 57 per cent of participants had changed their dietary, drinking or smoking habits, and 24 per cent felt that the level of their general health had improved. Significantly, 61 per cent reported uplift in mental well-being, this led to the setting up of 'Arts on Prescription', which is reported on in the next chapter. GPs who support the 'Exercise on Prescription' scheme have reported that it is a good way to get people to start taking regular exercise, and is a positive alternative to advice or drugs in the prevention of ill-health.

Exercise is good for your mental health

The benefits of physical exercise for individuals with mental health needs are many. Physical activity has the potential to improve the physical and psychological quality-of-life for people with mental health needs.[2] These people have the same physical-health needs as the general population, although their physical health can also be adversely affected by the effects that prescribed medications can have on cardiovascular functioning and weight. Exercise has also been shown to raise mood and reduce anxiety. It is also associated with improved sleep and body image, and raised self-esteem.

Recognising that exercise has an important role in decreasing depression and in reducing anxiety led Calderdale Borough Council to establish an 'Exercise on Prescription' service for individuals with mental health needs. This provides a tailor-made service for such people to enable them to access the facilities of council-run leisure services. The level of the support provided has ensured that individuals who have been referred have benefited well from the scheme, and have maintained their participation in activity. However, compared with their 'Exercise on Prescription' project for people with chronic heart disease and high blood pressure, the number of participants is low. People with mental health needs often require more support to access services, which needs to be reflected in the funding for such services.

Exercise can be used to break down barriers to learning

Building on the success of such GP referral schemes, Kent Adult Education Service (KAES) set up the 'Bodywise' health and fitness courses in Thanet in 1995. KAES is able to offer a wide range of physical activities, including: exercise to music, medan rhythmic movement, movement for older people, dance and exercise, circle dancing, yoga, fitness training, sequence dancing, line dancing, swimming, exercise in water, meditate and relax, relaxation, Shiatsu, Tai Chi, reflexology, homeopathy, and look after your back. This enabled GPs to refer a wider range of people. People referred through 'Bodywise' get a 50 per cent reduction to the advertised price of the course they choose, on the basis that the courses were running anyway and learners were filling unfilled places on courses.

KAES have taken, not surprisingly, the same approach to students enrolling on these courses as they would to any other student enrolling on a course.[3] Students get advice and guidance as to which is the most appropriate course for them. They are encouraged to complete a health diary, which is signed by the tutor. This encourages weekly contact with the tutor, so that progress can be monitored and any difficulties that have arisen may be discussed. Students are encouraged to change, rather than drop-out, if their initial choice is not suitable. Classes take place in a variety of venues, so that students can choose an environment in which they feel comfortable. Many of the activities on offer are group activities, and some participants enjoy the social aspect.

The approach taken by KAES has proved very successful. In the first year, 73 per cent of participants completed their course and 76 per cent of these noticed an improvement in their health. In an evaluation, students reported:

'I have gained so much confidence.'

'I have a general feeling of well-being.'

'My blood pressure is lower and I feel lighter.'

Using GP referral schemes in this way can also be a strategy to recruit new learners.

Many referrals to the KAES 'Bodywise' scheme are people who have not previously accessed adult education. By working alongside healthcare staff, KAES have been able to widen participation in learning to people who might not have previously considered learning. As such, the 'Bodywise' scheme breaks down the barriers to learning for some people. In the first year, 65 per cent of referrals were new learners and 38 per cent had introduced friends to adult education. This shows that such inter-agency working between learning and health has many benefits. Individuals have improved health from receiving support to exercise regularly, and health and wider benefits are associated with participation in learning. Health services are enabled to improve the health of their patients, and education services attract new learners.

A recent survey conducted by NIACE *Sport—A Leap Into Learning* has shown that those most likely to participate in sport or fitness activity are male, young, in higher social classes, students and those in full-time employment.[4] However, the survey also shows that 40 per cent of those who have not participated in learning for more than three years, and 27 per cent of those who have done no learning since learning in full-time education, are current or recent participants in sports or fitness activities. The findings show that these respondents are likely to be male, in their late twenties/early thirties, or over 55, in lower social classes and unemployed or retired. Aldridge concludes that reaching these groups through their interest in sport may prove to be an effective strategy for widening participation in adult learning. One of the most common barriers to participation in sport or fitness activity was feeling too old, ill, or disabled.

The kind of partnership work shown by KAES with 'Bodywise' and CEDC in their 'Alive and Kicking' initiative, targets certain groups of people and hooks into their motivations to participate, and provides sensitive and appropriate support to access activity in environments in which they are comfortable. Working with healthcare staff may enable adult education services and leisure services to successfully provide these supports.

Exercise can be a social occasion and a learning experience

Walking is one of the most health-improving activities. It is also an important strategy in health improvement because it does not require costly equipment or training, nor depends on attending a specific venue, and is therefore accessible to people across all socio-economic groups.[1] However, for some people it may be difficult to access safe or pleasant places to walk, and pollution and poor air quality is also an issue in some parts of cities.

A partnership between healthcare professionals, the local council and the residents of a housing estate, called the

'Christchurch Community Spirit Challenge', overcame some of these difficulties by reclaiming parts of the estate and nearby wasteland, and turning them into a trim trail. This then became a safe and pleasant place to walk. Residents have also learnt about committee structures, bid-writing, and other skills of community involvement and gaining resources. Walking can also be a social activity, participants sometimes barely realise how far and for how long they have walked, because they are engaged in conversations along the way.

These are some of the benefits that the Countryside Agency, who have developed a partnership with the British Heart Foundation, hope to realise through the setting up of their 200 health walks. The rationale is that when people

A 'Walking for Health' group grew out of an exercise class that took place at an Asian Women's Centre in Keighley. The women participating in the exercise class became more aware of the benefits from exercise for their health and wanted to do more, so the walking group was started. There are now about 40 or more women who meet regularly to walk. The tutor organiser plans routes, and directions are supported by photographs of local landmarks for walkers to spot along the way.

Many of the women have reported improved health, including feeling more relaxed, improved sleep and, for some of the older women who live alone, an improved appetite. The walk is also a very social event and often incorporates a picnic lunch. This ties in with the 'Five Fruit or Vegetables a Day' campaign promoted at the centre, as women are encouraged to think about how they can prepare healthy picnic food. The walking group is also a learning experience. All women have learned to make better use of facilities and services, including, for example, how to get the council to open bye-ways and clear thickets. The women have also developed a greater awareness of the countryside and of the history of the area. For many women English is their second language, and involvement in the group has improved their literacy, particularly in the use of public transport.

enjoy a good walk they are often working harder than they realise, and making more of their surrounding countryside and appreciating it more.

The British Trust for Conservation Volunteers (BTCV) have also set up Green Gym sites alongside normal volunteer work. GPs can now refer patients to voluntary work restoring woodlands and building footpaths. The people who become involved in these activities often exercise harder than they think, and the social aspect can be very motivating, as well as providing people with a network of friends and acquaintances. Volunteers also learn about conservation and the techniques employed to restore and protect the countryside.

Exercise for older people

GP referral of older people to such schemes is particularly important. Exercise for older people can be crucial in maintaining muscle strength and suppleness, which can mitigate against falls. Thirty per cent of people over the age of 65 will experience a fall at least once a year, and this figure rises to 50 per cent in people over 80 years.[5] Falls and accidents are such a major issue that the Department of Health made the reduction of accidents one of their targets in *Saving Lives : Our Healthier Nation*.

Supported exercise programmes, such as 'Exercise on Prescription', 'Walking To Health' and 'Green Gyms' also provide older people with social activity. Older women are more likely to live alone than older men, and involvement in exercise can provide access to social networks.[1] When exercise programmes are combined with learning through conservation voluntary work, they can also provide mental stimulation. In Christchurch, for example, 'Walking to Health' was set up in partnership with the University of the Third Age to produce guided walks that give details of landmarks along the way which are of particular local or historical interest.

In Berkshire, a preventative 'Keeping Active' project has been set up in partnership between social services, Adult Education, Berkshire Health Promotion Service and Newbury College. The pilot project offers a combination of Tai Chi and chair-based exercise, along with adult learning activities for mental stimulation, in day centres and residential homes. The evaluation of the project showed that about a third of participants reported improvement in their physical well-being and, significantly, over half reported an increase in self-confidence and increased enjoyment of life, particularly among people who had previously described their health as fair or poor.

An important aspect of the evaluation was the useful information that it provides on how adult educators can work in day centres and residential homes with older learners. Such issues as working in unfamiliar environments, the importance of support from care staff, and physical difficulties and limitations of residents, indicate how partnership-working needs to pay attention to detail at the operational level, as well as at a strategic planning level.

It also raises the question as to whether a holistic approach is necessary for people over the age of 50. The prevention of falls is not only of concern to health professionals, but also to social services and education.

'For social services it is the deterioration of independence that is of concern...for education, it is the deprived quality-of-life, especially in accessing lifelong learning opportunities, that is of concern.'[5]

A shared concern can give rise to a more holistic and effective approach of combined physical activity and mental stimulation.

Summary

This chapter has described programmes where physical activity is promoted to encourage physical and mental health, and a greater sense of well-being. Approaches can be preventative or recuperative, but the most successful approaches tap into the motivations of individuals and groups, so that the physical activity can be adopted as part of the person's lifestyle. Successful approaches take a holistic approach, combining physical approaches with learning and social interaction.

References

1   Royal College of General Practitioners (1998). *Independent Inquiry into Inequalities in Health Report (The Acheson Report)*, Royal College of General Practitioners.
2   Mentality (2001). *Making It Happen, a Guide to Delivering Mental Health Promotion.*
3   Challis, J. (1996). 'Kent Adult Education Service, Health Promotion, Exercise', *Adults Learning* Vol.8 No 3, pp. 66–67.
4   Aldridge, F. (2001). *Sport—A Leap Into Learning. A Study of Participation in Sport and Fitness Activities in Great Britain*, NIACE, unpublished.
5   Minter, C., Speed, J. (2000). *Keeping Active: A Multi-Agency Approach to the Problem of Fall*, unpublished.

Nottingham Castle Museum 'Up in Smoke' Project

4

Arts and health

Arts for positive mental health

The 'Arts on Prescription' project in Stockport was set up in 1996 for people with mild to moderate depression and/or anxiety problems, with the stated aim:

> 'to increase the level of mental well-being of participants using a wide range of creative processes.'

A psychiatric nurse assesses referrals, to see whether they would benefit from 'Arts on Prescription'. Those entering the project undertake arts activities, such as painting, drawing, creative writing and drama for 12–15 weeks. After this initial course, learners then progress onto a further course funded by the local college.

The project has been evaluated using the General Health Questionnaire. It showed that participants' mental health did not deteriorate and for many it improved.[1] The evaluation also showed that they used health resources less when they were involved in the project, and accrued other benefits, such as increased social interaction and increased use of other leisure and arts facilities.

As one participant said of his creative writing group:

> 'It helps me get out of the house and I am able to forget problems completely for a couple of hours.'

Another person described involvement with the project as:

'A light in the darkness of depression, both socially and expressively.'

Arts as a means of expression

It is exactly this chance to lose yourself in words, colours or music that makes the arts such a powerful force linking learning and health. The opportunity to use the imagination as a way of connecting with feelings, or to express feelings, is very empowering. In the arts, feelings and thoughts are what make people unique. Recognising such feelings and expressing them can be incredibly creative, as well as a learning process. Furthermore, it can be a safe way to express difficult and poerful emotions. In any human situation, however difficult or traumatic, there is often the opportunity to find some relief or resolution. Rising to this challenge requires creativity and often a new way of thinking, and in the process will involve profound and often intensely personal learning for individuals, communities and societies.

Courses set up by the Community Connections project in Nottingham used arts as a positive learning experience for users of mental health services. The tutor was determined to get away from the notion of arts as a therapy, and therefore based in a deficit model, and instead introduced arts as a learning experience. 'Introduction to Literature' and 'Creative Writing' courses were set up for people with enduring mental health difficulties, in the community and in secure environments. The tutor commented:

'it seems that when people become mental health service users, all their identities are stripped away and replaced with 'ill person' as an identity. Providing learning opportunities gives people an identity as a learner, but literature and creative writing gives people other identities, as writer or poet. Literature gives people access to other lives, people can read and think "I feel like that", it lessens the sense of isolation and can enable a new understanding.'

Arts for learning

Attending art, music or any other creative opportunities gives people the chance to learn how to look, listen, feel and interpret things. Students often talk of their ability to see things, themselves and their surroundings, differently as a result. It also encourages individuals to use their minds differently, to think creatively and laterally. It is, in a sense, gentle exercise for the mind. One student who attended a drawing class set up specifically for people with mental health difficulties said:

'In my drawing class I learned that, to see things clearly, sometimes you have to stand back to get a sense of perspective. I've sort of applied that principle to things in my life that stress me out. Instead of letting myself get too close to my problems and getting overwhelmed by them, I make myself stand back and apply a sense of perspective, and see them for how big they really are. Plus the added bonus of actually finding drawing relaxing.'

Wigan and Leigh College have set up play-writing courses for learners with mental health difficulties in secure environments. Learners write scripts on a diverse range of subjects that are then acted-out by students in performing arts at the main campus and video-taped. The learners within the psychiatric hospital can then watch their work the following week, and discuss the issues and how they have been portrayed by the students.

A recurring theme that is often mentioned by tutors and learners in these examples of good practice is not only the personal learning that individuals gain, but also the learning that groups do together. Groups of learners share ideas and experiences, as well as learn to work as a group.

An on-going project for Asian women in Keighley based at the Roshni Ghar, a day centre for Asian women with mental health needs, was designed for women who never have access, or have limited access, to arts activities. The women choose to learn silk painting and creative movement, such as classical Asian and Bollywood dance. The aims of the project have been to develop skills and confidence, build capacity and the ability to work in a group, to develop skills of observation and encourage an open attitude. The project also facilitates the development of ideas, and gives the opportunity for participants to explore choices and make decisions about their work.

The project evaluation showed the wider benefits of this arts-based work. The women noted such benefits as: 'good facial and physical exercise', 'fun and laughter', 'forget your problems for a little while', 'identified poor pelvic muscles and other health concerns', 'feel healthier', 'improved English' and 'improved confidence a great deal'.[2]

Using arts as a learning opportunity raises serious issues about good practice in teaching and learning. Engaging in arts can involve expressing thoughts, feelings and beliefs that can be quite personal and therefore require confidentiality. There is a degree of risk involved, and learners must feel that they can trust the tutor to respect their views and efforts. Feedback must be handled sensitively. As one tutor said:

'People's creative work is so much a part of them that if you criticise it, and concentrate only on spellings and grammar, or technique, rather than valuing the content, it can be very destructive to their sense of self and their creative expression. That can be very damaging...they may never put pen to paper again!'

Using arts to encourage greater use of cultural and social facilities

Another project to promote the arts as a strategy to improve health was the Kirklees Bibliotherapy project, which was set up to promote the benefits of fiction-reading to health professionals, people using health facilities, and library staff. Again, this project used literature, but it was beneficial in that it encouraged social interaction through reading groups and the increased use of facilities, such as libraries and other arts venues. Three bibliotherapists, working 18.5 hours each, were appointed to work in different areas of Kirklees. Two were based in libraries—one large, one small—and the third worked in an area served by mobile libraries. All areas were chosen for their high levels of social exclusion. One of the aims of the project was to promote the ideas of reading (particularly fiction) as an alternative to drugs, in the achievement of mental and physical well-being.

Like the Stockport 'Arts on Prescription' project, and indeed most other projects, hard data on health outcomes can be difficult to come by. However, the qualitative evidence from participants in these projects offers insights on their success in raising self-esteem and therefore serving as an impetus to making other changes in their lives. As one participant in the Kirklees project said:

'It's got me out of the house. I was stuck in a rut because I didn't go out much. I've met some new people and I've rejoined the library. Its encouraged me to look for new authors I wouldn't usually read.'[3]

Another woman decided that she would develop her literacy skills so she could help her children with their homework. Losing yourself in a good storyline can also improve your life by giving it some colour and adventure, or comfort and company. One mother experiencing post-natal depression reported that to escape into other worlds when she needed to was a source of release and support. An older man with cancer and feelings of loneliness found comfort and companionship in his last days through the reading group, and another woman put it succinctly when she said:

> 'Books are like friends to me, books are better than pills because you are in control.'

Involvement in these projects has also helped participants to be more culturally active and make better use of cultural and social facilities, often for the first time in their lives. One man, who had done the 'Arts on Prescription' course, later progressed onto an art course at college, and regularly visited local art galleries and his local library to borrow art books. Participants in the Kirklees Bibliotherapy project went to the theatre to see the dramatisation of a novel. It could be argued that these kinds of activity can enable people to perceive themselves differently, and to broaden their horizons and options.

These were some of the outcomes of a contemporary art show called 'Up in Smoke' that explored smoking issues. This consisted of work from international artists commissioned by the World Health Organisation, work by local primary school children, and photographic pieces by a group of ex-smokers. The ex-smokers—a group of six women and one man—had completed the 'New Leaf' smoking cessation course and decided they still needed to meet if they were to resist taking up smoking again.

The Health Action Zone Education Workstream provided funding for the show, and the outreach officer developed a programme that involved the ex-smokers working with a photographer to explore their experiences of quitting smoking and what it meant to give up. They created a visual image of their experience that formed part of the show—alongside work from international artists. A display folder documenting their experiences was also collated.

The positive outcomes from the photography course have been numerous. The group is a strong and committed self-help group that welcomes new members. They are committed to promoting smoking cessation and have encouraged family members and friends to give up. They have developed confidence to give talks on smoking cessation and are seeking funding to get their photographic images made into a calendar. They have learnt about photography, and have now requested a follow-on course from the museum on textiles. Importantly, they have all realised how much smoking had curtailed and limited their lives, in social terms as well as in terms of their physical health. As an increasing number of places become non-smoking environments, there were more and more places they wouldn't visit. As one woman eloquently put it:

'Before I did this course I had never been in a museum, my husband did, but I would always be outside having a fag.'

Evaluation of positive outcomes to arts and health work

The Centre for Arts and Humanities in Health and Medicine (CAHHM) is an independent research and evaluation resource based in the University of Durham. CAHHM investigates and promotes the practical applications and benefits of arts and humanities in healthcare.

CAHHM strives to do this by:

▶ evaluation of the effectiveness of the arts in patient-centred approaches to healthcare buildings and services;

▶ development of community-based arts in health and emotional literacy;

▶ learning development and training for medical students, artists and health professionals;

▶ creation of regional, national and international links in research and practice.

CAHHM is currently project-managing an initiative called 'Common Knowledge', a three-year arts in health development programme for the Tyne and Wear Health Action Zone. It is pioneering a new approach to placing arts activities at the heart of community health development and clinical practice. Across Tyne and Wear it has created a large network of artists, health professionals of all kinds, teachers, Local Authority officers, voluntary sector entrepreneurs, and community participants. This has led to the development of over 20 cross-sectoral pilot projects. Projects have ranged from use of live music in intensive care, to arts-led information designed for primary care, and embroidery with Alzheimer patients. Other activities include a mapping exercise of arts in health work across the Northern and Yorkshire region, an in-depth qualitative evaluation study of five community arts in health projects, the development of evaluation methodologies, and preparation of arts and humanities material for inclusion in the teaching of medical students.

The work of CAHHM is pioneering and innovative because it operates on several levels:

▶ It is attempting to put some form and definition to what we seem to instinctively and intuitively know—that creativity is positive and beneficial to health, but in a world where data and hard evidence are required to show worth and validity this can be hard to prove. The development of an evaluation methodology is crucial.

▶ Arts are often marginalised and under-funded, because they can be seen as peripheral and 'extra', but in reality creative and expressive arts go on all the time and touch our lives every day. Mapping the extent to which we use arts and creativity to promote health and social inclusion is a start to bringing it out into the open and giving it credence.

▶ Arts can be a solitary or individual way of expressing yourself, but it can also be communal. A celebratory sculptural lantern parade for the Wrekenton and Springwell estates began in 1994 and is now an annual event. From the outset it has involved hundreds of local children, their families, voluntary agencies, churches, and the area health-improvement team. The procession has become the distinctive event in the local calendar—a metaphorical 'screening' and celebration of community health. In the two-week period of lantern making leading up to the parade, health information on risk factors to the heart is imparted, and shared in a relaxed and domestic manner. As one local volunteer said:

'It's definitely made me think about my health and that of my kids, and given me the confidence to do something about it—we can choose to be healthier.'

One nine-year boy said:

'When the fireworks light up the heart, everyone is my friend.'

▶ Arts can also be a great equaliser. Arts activities do not rely on the written word to promote ideas and issues. This can be very empoering for people with basic-skills needs, people for whom English is not their first language, or people who think and learn visually. It requires different skills, and people with little formal education and low self-esteem can often discover hidden talents. Having a professional status does not make you any better at it than the users of services. It creates a level playing field, and there can be an interesting shift of power.

▶ Arts activities can be fun and social occasions, and they can be expressions of individual and communal feelings and emotions. As there can be no hierarchy of validity of the creative expression of thoughts and feelings, communal arts projects can be very inclusive, incorporating the work of children alongside adults, and that of friends and neighbours alongside strangers with whom you might unknowingly have shared experiences and understanding.

▶ CAHHM also works alongside healthcare staff to promote the incorporation of arts and humanities in their training and learning. Firstly, if there is an acceptance that arts are health-enhancing, then healthcare staff need to understand why and how they can promote art as a form of health-improvement activity. Secondly, healthcare staff have their own health and well-being to consider. In times of unprecedented levels of stress among healthcare staff, particularly GPs, creative expression may be an important outlet for their own emotions.

Summary

This chapter explores the link between arts learning and health, and shows that there are many outcomes. Arts can involve learning about health and improve health. Arts can be used for therapeutic outcomes, but they also offer a valuable opportunity for learning. Arts can also be communal, giving rise to the opportunity to share experiences, but also to increase social interaction and use of social and cultural facilities.

References

1   Huxley, P. (May 20th 1997). *Arts on Prescription—An Evaluation*, unpublished.
2   Kibble, J. (September 2001). *ACLF Report*, unpublished.
3   Morris, C. (July 2001). *The Kirklees Bibliotherapy Project, Final Report*, unpublished.

5

Self-esteem

Self-esteem is necessary for positive health and for learning

Self-esteem is often associated with mental health. People with positive mental health have good self-esteem, and those with mental health problems often have poor self-esteem.[1] Poor self-esteem potentially leads to mental health difficulties, but people with mental health difficulties may have poor self-esteem because they are among the most marginalised, stigmatised and excluded members of our society.

Self-esteem also has an impact on physical health. People in healthcare settings often need to make changes, or adapt their situation, due to chronic illness or disability or to prevent the onset of ill-health. Yet health practitioners are often faced with

> '…the grip of a paradox: so many patients are passive in the consulting room, yet to succeed with behaviour change they need to be active, vigilant decision makers.'[2]

Self-esteem also affects participation in learning. There are three major types of barriers to learning—cultural, structural and personal.[3] Personal barriers include lack of motivation, and low confidence and self-esteem. Those who feel they 'can't' do something face a greater barrier than those who 'won't'. Believing that you can't do something invariably means you don't do it. Low self-esteem and low motivation are seen to have a causal relationship.

Titus Alexander, Founder of the Self-Esteem Network, links positive self-esteem to accepting our achievements and short-comings, being able to take risks and adapt to change.[4] Increasing self-esteem increases emotional resilience, and gives individuals an emotional literacy that helps them cope with life and be assertive. People with good self-esteem are more likely to see things as being within their control, to see their potential for change, and to accept challenges and negotiate for help and support. Having a clear sense of your own self-worth may enable you to take realistic steps to adopt healthy behaviour and lifestyle. It may also help you to see what potential you have for learning for your own personal development.[5]

Strategies to raise self-esteem could therefore be said to have an important role in health improvement and, therefore, in the reduction of health inequalities and enabling learners to overcome the barriers to learning.

Raising self esteem in individuals and communities

A GP, Dr Anne Hayden, realised that many children coming to her surgery were experiencing emotional trauma through problems at home and at school. She set up the child and family counselling service that operated from the surgery, children's homes and local schools. However, she felt that if one could build self-awareness, self-esteem and confidence of parents and professionals looking after children and young people, this would really address the issues of low self-worth in youngsters and, therefore, in time, impact upon the community as a whole. In January 2001 she set up the ISECCA (Improving Self-Esteem and Confidence in Children and Adults) programme, which offers non-threatening personal development programmes and workshops to individuals aged 14 and over. The courses aim to help participants improve their self-esteem, self-efficacy and confidence, and the ability to succeed in all areas of life.

They provide an opportunity for individuals to recognise the habits, attitudes and beliefs that stop them from realising their potential, and gives them a toolkit with which they can take control of their own lives.

Potential—can do	Barriers Habits Attitudes Beliefs Expectations	Achievement— actually do

This is a diagram taken from training facilitated by Dr Hayden. It shows how negative habits, attitudes, beliefs and expectations can have a diminishing effect on achievements. If a person believes they cannot achieve something, or does not expect to achieve, this will adversely affect their chances of success. Hayden would also argue that if teachers, tutors or other professionals do not expect their learners, or service users, to achieve, then this will also negatively affect their chances of success.

ISECCA uses a whole-community multi-agency approach. In several disadvantaged areas, local schools work alongside representatives from the police; social services; education, health, drug and alcohol agencies; careers and youth services; community safety; youth offending teams; the church; and voluntary agencies, with the aim of raising standards in schools and reducing social exclusion. Other projects have involved working with officers and inmates in prison; speech therapy services; teenage pregnancy forum; school of nursing; working women's project (for prostitutes); GPs, hospital consultants and rheumatoid arthritis clinics. The projects will be able to evaluate what impact raising self-esteem has on individuals and communities.

Such a wide and diverse range of agencies conveys the message that:

▶ in transforming the lives of people and communities it is necessary to work with many individuals and agencies collaboratively;

▶ in working to raise the self-esteem of sections of communities deemed to be under-achieving due to low self-esteem, it is necessary to understand what self-esteem is;

> ▶ when individuals and agencies learn what self-esteem is, then they
> can adopt strategies to promote good self-esteem and understand
> how previous strategies may have undermined it.

Recognising the latter responsibility, Rollnick *et al.* write in their book *Health Behaviour Change. A Guide for Practitioners*:

'The origins of passivity do not lie only in the patients, but also in the way they are spoken to and dealt with by practitioners.'[2]

Similarly, in *Education's for Other People. Access to Education for Non-Participant Adults*, McGivney recognises the dispositional, or personal barriers that prevent people from learning, but also stresses that:

'Non-participation is an indictment not of public apathy but of an education system which still projects a narrow and elitist image.'[6]

Institutions, or individuals within institutions, can themselves inhibit the self-esteem of groups of individuals and, therefore, negatively affect their access to health services and chances of health improvement, as well as their participation in learning. This has led to community development initiatives, which take a holistic perspective on extending education and health to those most marginalised.

Learning about self-esteem to break down barriers to learning

The Workers Educational Association (WEA) South Eastern District and East Kent Health Promotion Service have set up Women and Health Groups. These are informative and informal health and self-awareness groups for women, which use learning about self and relationships, confidence building, assertiveness, stress management, communication skills, conflict management and opportunity awareness, as a strategy to build self-esteem and enable women to identify their own learning needs and make informed choices. Courses are free, and free childcare is always provided. In setting up the courses, women have a say in when and where they take place, and what the curriculum content will be.

Evaluations of the courses are positive, with women speaking of gains in confidence and self-esteem, and generally feeling happier and more assertive. Women made comments like:

'I'm so proud, so proud of all of us'.

Such gains have enabled the women to adopt better health behaviours, such as eating healthier foods, being more assertive about good diets, practising stress management techniques and using alternative therapies, and improved relationships with children. The impact that their learning had on their children was talked of time and again, with women explaining:

'I want to continue in learning because I think that if the children see me doing it then they will do it.'

'We were driving along one day and my husband made a comment about somebody. I said "Don't say that, it's unacceptable and I don't want to hear it and I don't want that sort of thing said in front of the children". Before I did these courses his comments would have gone right over my head'.

Participants also report a reduction in the use of other services, such as GPs and primary care, a reduction in the use of anti-depressants, and less reliance on social services and family centres. With their increased confidence and self-esteem, many women have continued in learning, including taking parenting and childcare courses, basic maths, pottery, literacy and vocational courses. Other women have started voluntary and community work, set up a self-help group, and one woman has started her own business. One woman said:

'Before I went on the course I thought that I would go back and work in Tesco when the children went to school, now that isn't good enough. I don't want to settle for that, I want much more than that. I want to go to university and eventually to work with young offenders.'

The community development approach of this work has attracted further partnership work with Kent Domestic Violence Forum, Lydd Rural Development Area Initiative, East Kent Parenting Strategy Development and HImPs.[7]

Several learning providers who have designated support services for people with mental health needs have set up learning programmes that look at issues such as confidence, self-esteem, anger management and decision making. Tutors on these commented:

'When we set up learning programmes specially for mental health service users I wanted to avoid the confidence and self-esteem type courses because they seemed to suggest a deficiency, as if we were saying that if you have mental health difficulties you must have low self-esteem. But people kept asking for them, so I had to give in to popular demand so to speak. And I have to admit that these courses are always full."

'Most of the learners have done courses on self-esteem when they have been in hospital or attending a day centre, but still seem to get something out of doing it again at college. Mind you I think that self-esteem is something you can do again and again and still get something out of it. Most of the people who do the courses choose to do them as a stepping stone to going on to do something else in college.'

These comments suggest that learners needed to learn about confidence before they had the confidence to learn. Many learners on such courses clearly see the link between what they have learnt and their improved sense of well-being. One man said:

> 'Before I started the courses I was a shy, introverted and anxious person. I wasn't very happy. The courses (on stress management and mental health awareness) have helped me to discover and to gain confidence. I feel empowered, and it isn't just what I have learned about myself and about my own mental health. It's what I have learned about other people and the different ways of looking at mental health... Also, I have been able to integrate the stress management into my everyday life and I am more focused... It's been like a personal revolution. It's been fantastic.'[8]

Another learner said:

> 'I did an anger management course. It was a revelation. I really believe now that if we were all taught to express our anger constructively we could do away with depression, ill-health, crime and violence. All that anger festering inside people, it has to come out somewhere. With me it was depression, I'm convinced of it.'[8]

Improving self esteem by removing barriers to learning

The strength of programmes like 'Women and Health' is that they reduce the factors that prevent participation in learning and which damage self-esteem such as:

- ▶ inability to pay for courses;
- ▶ inability to pay for childcare. Women on the women and health course stated that they would not have accessed the course if they had to pay for the childcare;
- ▶ insensitive or inappropriate publicity;
- ▶ courses held in accessible or intimidating environments;
- ▶ learning offered at an inconvenient time;
- ▶ being told what your learning needs are;

▶ insensitive, patronising or disrespectful attitudes from tutors, administrators or crèche workers.

At the same time, the programme provides a learning environment and curriculum that promotes self-esteem by

▶ defining self-esteem;
▶ teaching strategies to promote self-esteem;
▶ enabling participants to identify behaviours and situations that damage self esteem;
▶ teaching strategies for change and personal development.

Summary

This chapter is about self-esteem and shows that, to promote health and well-being, individuals need a positive sense of well-being. Feeling that you can't do something is a barrier to learning. Learning about self-esteem can therefore promote health improvement and widen participation in learning. Healthcare staff and learning providers also have a responsibility to understand and promote self-esteem, because we cannot raise self-esteem if we do not ourselves have self-esteem.

References

1   Carson, J., Harman, K., Webb, S., Kimonis, E., Kuipers, E. (June 2001). 'Assessing and measuring self-esteem in mental health: a comparison of scales in current use', *Mental Health Care*, Vol.41 No 10, pp.336–339.
2   Rollnick, S., Mason, P., Butler, C. (1999). *Health Behaviour Change. A Guide to Practitioners*, Churchill Livingstone.
3   Maxted, P. (1999). *Understanding Barriers to Learning*, Campaign for Learning.
4   Titus, A. (2001). 'Defining self-esteem. What is self-esteem and why does it matter? Self-esteem as an aid to understanding and recovery', *Mental Health Care* Vol.4 No. 10, pp. 332–335.
5   Field, L. (1993). *Creating Self-Esteem: A Practical Guide to Realizing Your True Worth*, Element Books.

6   McGivney, V. (1990). *Education's for Other People. Access to Education for Non-Participant Adults*, NIACE.

7   Wilma, F., Knight, J. (November 1988). *Report on the WEA South Eastern District's Women and Health Programme*, WEA South Eastern District.

8   Wertheimer, A. (1997). *Images of Possibility—Creating Learning Opportunities for Adults With Mental Health Difficulties*, NIACE.

6

Learning to feel better: prescriptions for learning

In 1999 the Institute for Employment Studies produced a report, *Learning in Later Life: Motivation and Impact*, which explored the nature and participation in learning of people aged 50–71; their reasons for participating; and the impact learning has on their health, family and social lives.[1] Eighty per cent of learners reported a positive impact of learning on at least one of the following areas: their self-confidence, how they felt about themselves, satisfaction with other aspects of life, and their ability to cope. Forty per cent reported an improvement in their ability to stand up and be heard, and/or their willingness to take responsibility. Twenty per cent reported an increased involvement in social, community and/or voluntary activity as a result of learning. Being disabled or in poor health was the biggest barrier to learning. However, when learners with disabilities or reporting poor health did participate in learning, they were more likely to report positive benefits of learning.

These findings were supported by the findings of the NIACE research *The Impact of Learning on Health*, which was quoted in Chapter 1.

Working in health settings

The concept of 'Prescriptions for Learning' came from several sources:

▶ 'Exercise on Prescription' and 'Arts on Prescription' were established, so why not more general learning opportunities on prescription?

▶ Many adult learners were saying that they had returned to learning because their GP advised them to, so what was it that GPs were seeing in individuals' health difficulties that they thought adult education could help with, and was adult education helping those individuals? Research undertaken by NIACE to explore this led to the report *The Impact of Learning on Health.*

▶ Adult educators who were working with individuals who were mental health service users were realising that, if these individuals had been encouraged to return to learning when they had first experienced mental distress, for example, when they first went to their GP, they might have felt the positive impact of learning earlier and the referral to mental health services might have been avoided.

The idea of 'Prescriptions for Learning' is simple. A learning adviser is based in a GP surgery, so that GPs and healthcare staff can refer individuals to discuss whether they want to access learning, what learning they want to do, and what support they might need to enable them to be successful in their learning.

Gloucester College of Arts and Technology (GLOSCAT) was the first college to set up a 'Prescriptions for Learning' type project. A community tutor was appointed to offer advice and guidance to patients in GP surgeries in the Gloucester and surrounding areas. This is now an established service, and the two part-time guidance workers work in 10 surgeries offering a 2½ hour session to each surgery. The service targets surgeries in areas of Gloucester, Cheltenham and Tewkesbury where there is disadvantage, poor health and low participation in learning. Up to April 2000 the support offered by the 'Learning for Life' service has resulted in approximately 100 new learners. Sue Allies, guidance worker for the service, feels that working in a health setting is really important, because people will not go elsewhere to access guidance and a guidance worker with knowledge of local education services and contacts can help individuals to make the step into learning.

The project is supported by Gloucestershire Local Education Authority Adult and Continuing Education and Training Service, NHS South West and Gloucestershire Social Services. The project has just won another three years' funding.

This approach to making contact with, and engaging with hard-to-reach learners was also the basis of a NIACE project in Nottingham.

In September 2000 NIACE set up a 'Prescriptions for Learning' project in partnership with the Greater Nottingham Learning Partnership, Nottingham Health Action Zone and East Midlands Development Agency.

NIACE appointed a Learning Adviser, who was seconded from Guideline Careers Service to work in three GP surgeries in South Nottingham, in areas of deprivation, poor health and low participation in learning. The Learning Adviser offered two sessions per week in each surgery. Initially, time was spent in the surgeries talking to healthcare staff and raising awareness of the project, raising awareness of the impact of learning on health, and building good relationships with healthcare staff. Referrals for learning have increased so that, in the first year of operation, there have been approximately 120 individuals referred for learning. The Learning Adviser works with individuals to help them identify what learning they might like to do, works with individuals to help them overcome some of the barriers to learning and provides on-going support to enable them to succeed and progress in their learning. The project has now extended to offer the service in six GP surgeries.

While there are slight differences in the way that the GLOSCAT and the Nottingham projects work they do share common issues. Evaluation of these projects confirms that basing a learning adviser in GP surgeries is an effective way of targeting hard-to-reach learners. In the evaluation of the GLOSCAT project, the majority of the participants were under 36 years of age, and were predominantly on low income and economically inactive. The participants were also socially inactive, with approximately 80 per cent of participants having no involvement with community or voluntary work, clubs, societies or Churches, nor attending films, talks or nightclubs. Nearly 70 per cent rarely or never participated in sport. The majority of the samples were generally healthy individuals who reported feelings of ill health, such as stress and fatigue.

The report states:[2]

> 'The absence of anything to engage their minds, with the lack of physical activity, might be causing the stress and fatigue. The activity of having to attend a course, or learning opportunities offered through this project could help to focus and engage their minds, help them to come out of the surgery and into mainstream life.'

In the Nottingham project, evaluation showed that of the 49 individuals who had been referred in the first four months, over half had not accessed formal learning since they left school at 16 years or earlier. Significantly, two-thirds of those evaluated were not involved in any community activities, clubs or societies. They did not go anywhere except to the shops and to the surgery, therefore learning providers had little chance of making contact with them. The majority of them said that they saw adverts for learning and picked up prospectuses, but did not have the confidence or motivation to do anything about them. Eighty per cent of the individuals who were evaluated said they would not have accessed learning without the help of the project.[3]

Although working in healthcare settings is an effective way to target hard-to-reach learners, it is not without its difficulties:

► Healthcare staff may have no experience, or out-dated experience of adult, community or further education. They may perceive that adult education only offers academic or vocational qualifications, which they may judge to be inappropriate, or even harmful, to their patients.

► Healthcare staff may not see learning as being an activity that can promote health and well-being. They may not think of learning as an activity that can be social, fun, improves self-esteem and confidence, increases physical activities, or acts as a stepping-stone to employment and improved quality-of-life.

Both these factors mean that healthcare staff may unwittingly become the gatekeepers to the service.

Other factors include:

► healthcare staff are very busy people with huge demands upon their time;

► working as an educationalist in a healthcare setting, and therefore working in a professional setting outside of your own profession, can be very isolating.

Both the Learning Advisers for the GLOSCAT and the Nottingham project say that investing time to overcome these barriers is crucial.

It is also important to keep the project in the minds of healthcare staff. Both workers make sure that they spend time at each surgery making their presence felt. Sue Allies at GLOSCAT said,

'Even if I haven't got any appointments booked I still go. I use that time to talk to staff and tell them about things'.

Other strategies that Sue Allies and Mike Slaney of Nottingham have used include:

► getting on to the team-meeting agenda in order to talk about your project;

► joining staff at coffee times, so that they get to know who you are;

▶ winning the support of the Practice Manager, who can help you to remind staff;

▶ encouraging people to feedback to the doctor or other healthcare staff about their successes in learning and the benefits to their health;

▶ producing a newsletter that has a 'league table' of referrals from each surgery, a breakdown (anonymous) of the number of referrals who are accessing learning and what they are doing, quotes from learners highlighting their successes and their pleasure in learning, as well as other articles of interest to healthcare staff;

▶ making sure you have representation from healthcare staff on your steering group. They will be able to help you identify other strategies as you go along.

It makes you think

The following article appeared in a newsletter to information, advice and guidance services, but it could easily be used for inclusion in a newsletter to healthcare staff.[4]

Read the following case studies and discuss with colleagues which people you think would benefit from a confidential chat with a Learning Adviser.

▶ Bill, 54, worked as a manager until he was made redundant six months ago. He is on medication for depression and has resigned himself to an early retirement.

▶ Karen is 19, has a young baby and shares a flat with her boyfriend. She has regular visits from a health visitor and confides that she regrets leaving school before taking GCSE's.

▶ John is 74 and recently lost his wife. He visits the surgery regularly and is very lonely.

▶ Jane has MS. She uses a wheelchair and her husband has given up work to care for her.

▶ Ann, 36, works as a receptionist and would like more confidence.

▶ Sean is 29 and is a recovering drug user. He has not worked for nine years. He can sometimes be aggressive in the surgery.

Another way to ensure that the project effectively reaches out to all potential learners is to by-pass the gatekeepers:

▶ Set the project up so that referral is not restricted to one or two key individuals and anybody can refer. Receptionists, for example, may have more time and know peoples' personal situation well enough to judge whether learning might be of interest to them. Furthermore, when receptionists refer individuals it can seem less 'medical'.

▶ Encourage self-referral by putting up posters, or having leaflets available in the surgery. Publicity in community languages is also crucial in some areas.

▶ Produce a patients' newsletter, which gives quotes from individuals who have accessed the service and the benefits they have experienced.

▶ Set up a learning noticeboard in the surgery.

▶ Raise awareness of the impact learning can have on the health of certain groups. For example, through monitoring referrals in Nottingham it became apparent that people aged over 60 were not being referred. An article in the newsletter was written, and a strategy explored to raise awareness of the health impacts for learners aged 60+.

▶ Do not restrict referral on the basis of certain diagnoses. The only criteria for learning should be that it might be of interest to an individual. However, this openness of approach can be quite off-putting, as it may seem too vague. The GLOSCAT project overcame this by producing a referral guide outlining groups of people, e.g. unemployed people, single parents or people with certain diagnoses—e.g. depression, anxiety, high blood pressure—who might benefit from learning. This actually included most of the people who attended the doctor's surgery!

Both the Nottingham and the GLOSCAT project have found these strategies useful in increasing the number of referrals to their projects. Slowly, over time, the Learning Advisers themselves have been accepted as valued members of a team working for health improvement, and learning has become recognised as a strategy for health improvement. It has become less isolated for the members of staff, and the rewards of the investment of time have become ever more apparent.

The evaluation of both the projects shows that the support of healthcare staff is crucial for success. In Nottingham and Gloucester healthcare staff view the projects positively, as one GP in Nottingham remarked:

'It is visionary because it recognises that health is bigger than medicine.'

Another GP said:

'It is somewhere for me to refer "heartsink" patients and that feels good for me.'

A health visitor in Gloucester wrote:

'The "Learning for Life" project offers our patients the chance to increase their confidence and self-esteem, and has resulted in many happier individuals, especially those who go on to achieve a qualification. The "buzz" they get from their achievement has supported some people into employment and/or further study.'

Healthcare staff have found that the service does not add to their workload, but actually supports their work in trying to improve the quality-of-life for their patients.

An educational guidance approach

Although the 'Prescriptions for Learning' model is essentially a strategy to widen participation in learning, the focal activity of that strategy is guidance. It is, however, more than the information and advice usually provided for adults.

The essential characteristics of this model of guidance are:

▶ it is provided in outreach settings, in this case, healthcare settings. Many of the adults referred by healthcare staff do not have the confidence to access mainstream guidance provision in careers offices, adult guidance services, or colleges. The guidance takes place where an individual feels comfortable. One person said:

> 'I saw him at the surgery. I have agoraphobia so I was more relaxed because I know the place. I was more able to talk.'

▶ it is very person–centred and individualised. The guidance interview is conducted at the individual's own pace and concentrates on what issues they need to explore and resolve;

▶ it is not time-limited. The first guidance interview may last 45–60 minutes, but there may be several appointments after that before an individual feels that they have made an informed choice. Individuals sometimes feel overwhelmed by the barriers they feel prevent them from learning. These may be external barriers, like costs, childcare or travel; or health barriers, such as coping with pain, anxiety or limited physical mobility. Or there may be internal barriers, such as a lack of self-esteem and confidence. As one student said:

> 'In my situation it will take more than a quick-fix solution.'

Time taken to address all these barriers is imperative. If only half of the learners issues are addressed, the learning adviser runs the risk of raising expectations without ensuring success and they will have wasted both the learner's time and their own;

▶ the guidance process may involve some practical activity, like visiting a learning provision so a person can see what it is like—particularly important when a person may not have stepped inside a college or adult learning centre in their adult life. Short taster courses can also help people decide whether it is for them, and the learning adviser can help them pick up the issues after trying something out;

A learner on the Nottingham project said:

'I did a three-hour computer taster-course, it wasn't for me. It made me realise I'm a people-person, but at least I tried it.

▶ Guidance should also be an on-going process. An individual may enrol successfully for a ten-week course, but at the end of it they may need to reflect on what they have learnt and what the next step will be. When people know that the guidance worker is there for them they use the service as a safety net when they need to get their learning back on track. One young mother said:

'It's nice to know I can pick up the phone and get help.'

Guidance as a learning process

From the evaluation of 'Prescriptions for Learning' projects it is apparent that the guidance process is a learning process for many individuals. Guidance can offer an opportunity to become more self-aware. Individuals can explore and reflect upon their interests, abilities and values. They also have an opportunity to look at some of the blocks to their moving on. Individuals can also explore their preferred learning environments and learning styles.

One woman said:

'It was helpful, but I didn't realise how helpful until I sat down at home without distractions and thought about all we had talked about. The truth had come out; it had helped because I got a clearer view of my likes and dislikes. I understood myself more.'

For many people referred to the Nottingham project there is a need to think about making a change in their lives. Perhaps an individual can no longer continue in their job because of injury, or they have experienced bereavement of a partner.

The guidance worker in Nottingham observes:

'Most of the patients seen during this pilot project have great difficulty in acknowledging that their life is no longer going to pursue its familiar pattern. Whatever symptoms propelled them into a doctor's surgery, and from there to an interview with the Learning Adviser, they are now going to have to face change. That means drawing a line under what they have been, learning how to think positively about themselves, and learning new personal, as well as practical skills. In order to make this transition successfully they need considerable support, emotionally, as well as practical...'[5]

When individuals get to a stage where they feel motivated to make changes in their lives, they can then feel overwhelmed by the options and the choices available to them. Support to identify the right course; make sense of the jargon attached to learning; and sort out travel routes, care arrangements, costs and entitlements to funding is essential. A skilled guidance worker would do it in such a way as to enable the learner to retain control of the problem-solving and decision-making process.

Guidance can also be an opportunity-awareness process. Learners get the chance to explore what the options are, where sources of information are, and what they may be entitled to. Importantly, the guidance worker can help an individual become more assertive in claiming the support and funding to which they may be entitled.

As one man put it:

'I've been on the streets since I was 14. I never realised there were so many possibilities.'

For many individuals, initial education is marked by feelings of failure, misery, or boredom. Adult years may be marked by unemployment, or by jobs with little challenge, satisfaction, or opportunities to fulfil potentials. Years may have been spent caring for others, putting their needs before your own. Limited income will limit leisure opportunities, and options for hobbies and pastimes. In these situations, it will be hard for a person to know what they are good at, what they are interested in, or what potential they have. This is particularly true if you are depressed and low, downhearted, or in pain much of the time. Consequently, an expectation that learning goals, career ambitions, or even a plan to do something for leisure or personal interest, can be arrived at simply by providing information and advice, or a one hour guidance interview, is unrealistic. It may work for people who are confident, optimistic and have already invested in their own learning and skills; but for others who have experienced years of exclusion, limited opportunities, loss of confidence, ill health or non-participation, the support needs to be more in-depth and on-going. However, it is not limitless guidance, because individuals, having gone through this learning process with the resulting increase in confidence and self-esteem, usually become more independent in their learning. Many will have acquired the confidence for participation in life-long learning.

Guidance can also be a learning process for the learning adviser and for the organisation. In more traditional guidance interventions, the guidance process may be condensed into the usual 45–60 minute slot; and if an individual seeks further guidance they cannot be assured that they will see the same guidance worker again. In these situations the guidance worker cannot see how effective their guidance was, as there are no opportunities for feedback. In the GP surgery model of guidance, the learning adviser keeps contact with the individual, and can gain some insight into how the guidance process is helping that person.

Guidance can also provide organisations with an increased awareness of the learning needs of communities. In Chapter 2, the role of health visitors was noted as being a positive means of collecting individual health stories, which build up into a picture of collective health needs in the community. Similarly, a guidance worker may hear the individual learning stories and, from there, can identify collective learning needs. This method has been used by learning providers who, through guidance with individual learners with mental health needs, have been able to build up a responsive curriculum for mental health service users.

The health impact of guidance

When the 'Prescriptions for Learning' projects were set up it was expected that by returning to learning people would experience positive health benefits. However, individuals began to experience health benefits after their first meeting with the learning adviser. An earlier evaluation of the Gloucester project had also shown this to be true.[6]

▶ Individuals reported that they felt listened to by the learning adviser. Many were well aware that other professionals, particularly healthcare staff, just do not have the time that they need to tell their whole story. The fact that the learning adviser gave them 45–60 minutes made them feel valued, and that they mattered.

All participants in the Nottingham project referred to this:

> 'Most professionals just don't have time these days. The fact that he took time was so uplifting and I felt reassured. So much in the system puts you down, but he said I could do it. It just felt really good.'

> 'Being listened to. In four years since my accident no one has listened to what I want and what I worry about. I thought I was going mad.'

▶ By working through all the issues and concerns that individuals had, and by working in a person-centred way, people reported feeling more in control. A sense of being active and doing something to change their situation felt good for many people, and gave them a sense of hope. For example, one man said:

> 'It's more the fact that I'm doing something to change my situation rather than the actual learning that makes me feel better. Being active, making decisions, rather than being passive.'

If you believe that your feelings are valued, that what you think is important, and that you can take control over your decisions and actions, then you will develop a sense of empowerment. It is a sense of self-empowerment that enables individuals to take action. It creates an increased sense of self-esteem, which is also conducive to further action, but is essential to a sense of well-being.

The health impact of learning undertaken following guidance

In an evaluation of the Nottingham 'Prescriptions for Learning' project, individuals who have enrolled on courses as a result of guidance were asked whether they felt that learning had an impact on their health. The responses were positive and fell into three categories, mental well-being, physical well-being and wider benefits.[7]

Mental well-being was most often cited by learners.

▶ Almost all learners reported raised confidence and self-esteem.

▶ A more general feeling of cheerfulness and uplifted mood was also frequently mentioned.

One woman said:

> 'Yesterday, I looked in the mirror and smiled at myself for the first time in four years.'

▶ Some people also talked about feeling more optimistic and hopeful for their future. A typical comment was:

> 'A light at the end of the tunnel I could aim for. There was some hope. I've been suicidal, thinking I'm going nowhere.'

Some people also noted an improved physical well-being.

▶ People who experienced pain most or all of the time did not feel that it lessened their pain, but felt that it distracted them from dwelling on it. Some also talked of being able to cope with it more effectively and to put it in perspective more readily. Instead of it being all-consuming, they now accepted it as being there alongside other more positive or enjoyable activities. Being physically more active was also realised to be a benefit, and some also thought that getting involved with learning gave them the impetus to get out of the house.

▶ Improved sleeping was another physical benefit that was mentioned by learners.

▶ For some individuals there were direct identifiable physical health improvements, such as lowered blood pressure.

These health benefits were immediate. Learners reported these positive benefits to learning four months after the project was begun. Further evaluation will investigate what the longer-term benefits to individual's health and well-being are, and whether the initial boost to self-esteem and physical health is maintained.

For many individuals there were wider benefits to getting involved with learning.

▶ Becoming more out-going, developing new friendships, and wider support networks. Some people also mentioned being assertive in talking to strangers, professionals and asking more questions and for help when they needed it.

One woman said:

'Yes, I get the chance to get out more and I take the baby out more. I'm mixing with all kinds of people. The benefits are for everything—for my kids, for a job. I don't want to be a burden on anyone.'

▶ Changes in the way they inter-related with their families and others were also noted. This included having more to talk about at home and to their partners, and greater attention to children and their future prospects. One man who was a carer for his disabled wife commented on how their relationship had improved since they had both started learning. He was reassured that his wife's needs had been taken care of when she was doing her course, leaving him free to get on with his learning. Previously, they had spent all their time together. Now when they come back from college they had things to tell each other, and found that because they weren't as bored and frustrated, they argued less.

▶ Some people also talked about improved prospects for the future. This included unemployed people, but also people who were off work due to illness, or who were vulnerable to being signed-off sick. One woman who was experiencing physical difficulties with the work that she did and was becoming increasingly depressed talked of how she could see herself 'spiralling downwards'. She had taken some time off work with stress and anxiety, and could see this becoming more frequent if not permanent. Some sessions with the learning adviser enabled her to put her 'escape route' into action. Knowing that she would have to brush up on her literacy skills, she started to read at home, which also took her mind off her immediate problems.

▶ The importance of the 'Prescriptions for Learning' type of project is that it takes guidance into settings where there are non-participants in learning, and where individuals feel comfortable to talk about their learning needs. The strong focus on on-going and in-depth guidance also allows for a diversity of learner's needs to be met. It could be argued that, because individuals have had more time to clarify their learning goals and discuss their learning needs, they are more likely to access the most appropriate learning opportunities. Hopefully, the strong element of pre-course and on-going guidance will improve retention and achievement. Further evaluation on the Nottingham project aims to find out whether this is true or not.

Health and basic skills

It has to be stressed that not everybody with mental health difficulties or poor health has basic skills needs and, therefore, the individualised approach of the 'Prescriptions for Learning' model is important in that it allows for the diversity of learners' needs. The approach of learning providers who use guidance in their work to enable access to learning for mental health service users also allow for this diversity. Learners with mental health needs have a huge diversity of learning needs, and working with individuals enables learning advisers to identify these and provide any necessary support, including, where appropriate, support for basic skills.

There is a correlation between basic skills needs and depression. People with basic skills needs have more limited opportunities, which will tend to lead to disadvantage, poverty and poorer health. A survey conducted by the Basic Skills Agency showed that women with very low literacy were five times as likely to be classified as depressed as those with good skills.[8] Men with very low literacy skills were three times more likely to be classified as depressed as those with good skills. The survey explored this further, and found that men and women with very low literacy scored significantly higher on questions relating to not feeling in control over events in their life, feeling unable to trust others, and not feeling that they get what they want from life. They also scored significantly lower when asked whether they felt satisfied with life.

The Health Development Adviser for a Primary Care Trust and the Essential Skills Co-ordinator at North and West Essex Adult Community College, worked in partnership to address what they saw as a multi-dimensional problem of poor basic skills of adults in Harlow. They decided on a two-pronged approach. Firstly, they set about raising awareness of the issues with all front-line staff in healthcare settings. Training was provided to help staff look at causes of poor basic skills, how often we use basic skills in our everyday lives, how basic skills impact on health, and how people with poor basic skills do not have equal access to public services. The training also looked at whether the leaflets and literature available in public services meet the needs of people with poor basic skills.

The second part of the approach was to set up a peer advisory group, made up of past and present basic skills students. The purpose of the group was to inform agencies and learning providers how those with low basic skills would like them to respond to their needs. Courses that built basic skills into learning about health were taken out into the community. By working in partnership with housing associations, older people's services, health visitors and midwives it was hoped to engage with people who would not normally come forward for help with their basic skills.

These findings were the catalyst for a project in Harlow. Encouraging adults to take up learning to address their basic-skills needs can be very challenging.

▶ People may associate reading and writing with feelings of failure, and of feeling bad about themselves.
▶ People may associate the thought of returning to learn with schooling, which might have been a time of bad experiences, and being made to feel stupid.
▶ People may be reluctant to disclose their basic-skills needs, feeling that they will be judged or ridiculed. They may be adept at covering up their difficulties, and feel unable to reveal the extent to which their basic skills limit their lives.

Many basic-skills providers try to help people overcome these barriers by using strategies such as:

▶ introducing basic skills on the back of other issues that people feel more motivated by, for example, health issues, or parenting skills;

▶ working in partnership, so that staff from other agencies that the individuals may know and trust can be the ones to broach the subject and encourage them to take the step back into learning. This is why training for staff in agencies to spot basic-skills needs and make sensitive referrals is important;

▶ locating the learning in places where people feel comfortable, and which are not associated with 'school';

Middlesbrough Adult Education Centre chose to do some basic-skills work with St Luke's, the local psychiatric hospital, using some monies available through the Basic Skill Initiative. Two courses were set up in partnership with the occupational therapy department. Basic skills were integrated into the existing community-skills group run by the occupational therapists. This gave patients a means of accessing written information, and the opportunity to plan and evaluate visits. The use of a computer and digital camera proved very popular.

The second group used primary sources to discuss and write about their memories of St Luke's. All the courses were well attended and produced some interesting work, particularly the memories of St Luke's group. Many of the people on the wards had lived at the hospital for many years and their personal memories are fascinating. These histories have been collated into a booklet, which has been distributed outside the hospital. Patients hope this will reduce some of the fear and stigma about psychiatric hospitals and mental illness.

Through participating in the courses, people on the wards were able to improve existing skills, which for some meant that they were more able to participate in the daily routines of the wards. For others, participation in the courses enabled them to regain lost skills, including participating in discussions, ordering thoughts and writing descriptively.

It should be noted that there were also benefits for staff on the wards. Some staff saw patients in a different light, appreciating that they had more skills than they had previously realised. Working with the Adult

Education staff, they then made sure that they enabled patients on the wards to practice their skills and provided opportunities for their further development. Learning consequently became part of the long-term care plans that occupational therapists developed.

Some basic-skills awareness training was also provided for ward staff, so that they would fully understand what was meant by the term 'basic skills' and the impact lack of basic skills has on people's lives. As a result of this, hospital staff realised that a significant proportion of patients could not read the ward information pack given to people on admission. Furthermore, as part of the diagnosis and therapy, patients were often asked to write down their feelings and thoughts. Staff realised that when people failed to complete this task it was not necessarily non-compliance, but could be an inability to do it.

Education can also be bad for your health!

Some adults have had bad experiences of education, particularly during their initial education. This might be because certain learning needs were not addressed early on and they fell behind. Unless they have been given the chance to catch up later, they will have lingering feelings of failure and gaps in their learning. The obvious example of this is people who leave school with poor literacy or numeracy. For some adults, school is also associated with bullying and teasing. For others, education can be associated with pressure to achieve and never feeling that they are good enough.

Such experiences leave people with feelings of failure, of 'being thick', 'not good enough', or fear and humiliation. Schooling for some adults may even have been a time of the onset of mental health difficulties.

Enabling adults in this position to return to learning needs to be very sensitively handled. There are strategies to help adults overcome these emotional barriers, such as:

▶ working with individuals, such as in the 'Prescriptions for Learning' project, to identify their worries and fears. Learning advisers take on a mentoring role, and give reassurance that the individual can achieve;

▶ working with groups, such as the New Choices for Women course in Kent, which encourages peer support;

▶ taking time to identify the right learning programme, so that students enjoy their learning and can be successful;

▶ meeting people, so that they have somebody to walk into the college with them, or basing the learning in a comfortable and known environment;

▶ ensuring that the right learning support is available. This may involve taking the time to check that things are going well, or linking the learner to a 'study buddy'.

Overcoming such barriers and becoming a confident learner can give an enormous sense of achievement and a changed perception of self. As one woman said:

'I always thought I was thick because I didn't do well at school. Now I realise that the way they taught us at school just wasn't the way I need to learn. It was all copying off the board, but I am a talker and a doer, I learn by doing things.'

Another man said:

'All those things they said to me at school...going back and doing this is like putting two fingers up and to them and saying "I won!"'

Some adults, whether or not they have a bad experience in initial education, find returning to learning very stressful. In the research conducted by NIACE on 'The Impact of Learning on Health', some learners talked about the 'disbenefits' to learning.[9] For example, the stress and anxiety of having to maintain concentration, and the frustration of not being able to do something. Other health disbenefits can be tiredness, dissatisfaction with former life, and negative impact on relationships. However, many of the respondents said that, despite these, they were still glad they took up learning again. One woman said:

> 'Definitely stress. Before returning to learning I never had headaches and now I am rarely without one. Despite this, I would still do the same again. Headaches are better than boredom.'

Another woman said:

> 'I have suffered a broken marriage since starting back into education, but this is down to personal growth and new confidence.'

This is quite a common occurrence, sometimes referred to as the 'Educating Rita' syndrome.

For others the disbenefits were numerous. One woman wrote:

> 'Stress. I had to see a doctor during the last term at university. I am a single parent on a low income and I was probably trying to juggle too much, trying to cope with a hyperactive child, a degree course and finances together with family and relationship pressures. Meeting deadlines and exams meant more pressure for me'.

Learning can cause stress and pressure for learners, and it is imperative that learning providers are aware of the constraints of adults' 'outside' lives. Indeed, many providers do have strategies to support learners in difficulties. Having a person such as a learning adviser, as in the 'Prescriptions for Learning' model, is another way to support learners and can mitigate some of the disbenefits identified. Through effective pre-course guidance, factors that can impede success can be discussed and alternative programmes or sources of support can be identified. Some learners may be unaware of support structures in education and, even, of what support they can request. Having a learning adviser in an advocacy role can help give the support they need. According to one man participating in the Nottingham project:

'I have tried to access learning before but always ended up on the wrong course and ended up dropping out. I always blamed myself and it made me feel worse about myself. Spending time with Mike meant that I could see what had been my problem, and what course was right for me and help I could ask for.'

Summary

This chapter has described how providing guidance in health-care settings can enable learning providers to engage hard-to-reach learners and thereby widen participation. It also describes how guidance and learning can have immediate benefits to physical and mental health, and individual's sense of well-being. Raising healthcare staff awareness of the impact of learning on mental as well as physical health can ultimately improve access to healthcare for service users, which, in turn, has health impacts. It is also recognised that learning can also have negative health impacts, and that, to lessen these, it will be necessary to support learners to access appropriate learning opportunities and support structures within learning provision.

References

1 Dench, S., Regan, J., Great Britain Department for Education and Employment (2000). *Learning in Later Life: Motivation and Impact*, Department for Education and Employment.

2 Ahmed, S., Barnes, S. (2001). *Evaluation of Learning for Life/GP Project*, Bristol University, unpublished.

3 James, K. (2001). *Evaluation Report of 'Prescriptions for Learning'* Nottingham, NIACE, unpublished.

4 Watson, G., Allies, S. (Summer 2001). 'Report on Prescribing Guidance', *Gloucestershire Information, Advice and Guidance Partnership Newsletter*, No. 2 pp. 4.

5 Slaney, M. (Autumn 2001). 'Learning to Improve Patients' Well-Being', *The Patients' Network*, Vol.6 No. 2 pp. 34–35.

6   McGivney, V. (1997). *Final Evaluation of the Gloucester Primary Health Care Project*, NIACE, unpublished.
7   James, K. (2001). *Evaluation Report of Prescriptions for Learning*, NIACE, unpublished.
8   Bynner, J., Parsons, S. and Basic Skills Agency (1997). *It Doesn't Get Any Better: The Impact of Poor Basic Skills on the Lives of 37-year-olds*, The Basic Skills Agency.
9   Aldridge, F., Lavender, P. (1999). *The Impact of Learning on Health*, NIACE.

Part 3

Strategies to widening participation and improving health

For practitioners who decide to provide one-off sessions about certain health issues, who want to run a series of sessions, or who want to encourage regular activity or participation in learning, this section looks at some strategies of how you might put ideas into practice.

IT'S A BLOKE THING

"After a stroke at 47, the doc said to pack up smoking and take an aspirin a day. So I carried on smoking and took two aspirins until it was too late..."

What does it take to get a bloke to the doctor? How come many feel it's a bit of a woman's thing to talk openly about health?

"It's not very macho, is it, for a bloke to admit he feels bad? Especially if it's due to stress or feeling a bit down."

MEN'S HEALTH 2000

Walsall East Health Action Zone members decided to explore men's attitude to health on their own territory. Nurses and arts workers toured local pubs and clubs as part of Men's Health 2000 asking men about health and lifestyle, and offering on-the-spot check-ups.

"I couldn't believe it when I walked in the local and there was a nurse up the corner offering to take my blood pressure! My mate had a bit of a shock actually, because his was off the scale and she told him he really ought to see his doctor."

WHEN YOUR LIFE'S IN YOUR HANDS, BE A MAN- NOT A BLOKE'

Funded By Walsall East Health Action Zone

Walsall Community Arts Project

7

Putting ideas into practice

Getting started

This chapter is addressed to practitioners and looks at some of the practical issues of getting ideas off the ground. It looks at assessing need, using resources, building partnerships and funding.

Assessing need

Before you start it is important to assess need. For learning providers one way to do this will be to look at who is missing from the provision. Do you, for example, cater for the needs of older learners, homeless people, or people with mental health difficulties?

Local Learning and Skills Councils have to complete strategic plans, and Local Authorities have to put together Adult Learning Plans. Regional Development Agencies will have skills' action plans, to meet their plans for regional regeneration. A raft of data on employment opportunities, unemployment levels, income levels, qualification levels and, for example, participation rates will underpin these plans.

Healthcare staff may have identified key health issues in their locality that may be stated in the local HImPs. Mental Health Services need to produce plans for the National Service

Framework Standards. Meeting these plans or standards may help to identify needs. For example, low levels of skills among individuals in a region may highlight a lack of learning provision and opportunity in that area. Another example might be when mental health service providers, in meeting the standards of the National Service Framework, identify a lack of suitable learning and training opportunities for their service users. Practitioners working within health or learning may respond to an expressed need of individuals or groups.

It is first necessary to see what provision already exists in your location. There may be agencies that already exist to work with certain sections of the community and you may be able to tap into existing provision, adding in what you can uniquely provide. A crucial part of assessing need is to consult with potential participants in the project. However, as McGivney writes:

> '...the consultation process should not be a simple matter of asking what people want to learn but an in-depth dialogue which allows interests, needs and priorities to emerge'.[1]

What emerges may not be as you anticipate. For instance, Christchurch Community Spirit Challenge involved residents of local estates in a discussion about what they thought were the needs of their community. This resulted in the development of a trim trail and BMX track on the estate.

Deciding what to do

You may already have an idea of what you want to achieve. For example, the challenge that confronted Walsall Community Arts, was the raising of self-esteem in young people as a means to prevent risk-behaviours. They consulted young people, who were clear that they wanted song writing and music production opportunities. Walsall Community Arts worked with the young people using these media and produced a CD rom of the work that the young people had written themselves about their lives.

This led to the young people learning about musical production and song writing, and has had many other learning outcomes. It has also led to the young people being involved in local health improvement and the establishment of a young person's Health Action Zone work-stream.

Stockport's 'Exercise on Prescription' led to the setting up of the 'Arts on Prescription' project, in which people with mild to moderate mental health difficulties are referred to arts activities.

Your project may be time-limited, so when you make your plans you should think about what will happen when the project ends. Will the learners that you have worked with be supported to find further information or help, or to move on to the next stage? Will the organisation that you have worked in partnership with be able to continue the project? For example, sessions on chair-based exercise may be beneficial for physical fitness, but, like all exercise regimes, unless it is maintained the benefits will be lost in time. You need to ask yourself early on in what way your work will build the capacity of the organisation or community in which you intend to work. This thinking should also help you decide what to do.

Allowing time

Developing new work invariably takes more time than you realise. Time is needed to approach and talk to possible partners in your projects. You will also need time to identify resources, suitable tutors or workers, and a suitable venue. Unless you already have a group of learners, you need to build in time to recruit participants. Even when you have an identified group of learners it still takes time for them to feel relaxed in a learning environment. You also need to give time to the 'gatekeepers', for example, primary-care staff; managers and care workers in residential homes; youth workers or community workers. Winning them over and clarifying with them what you want to achieve will maximise your chances of success.

Setting up a steering group

At some point you may want to think about setting up a steering group. This can bring many benefits. These may include:

▶ providing a network of support and contacts for project workers;
▶ bringing a wide range of expertise, including possible sources of funding, through members;
▶ helping you to think about the barriers and difficulties that crop up and impede your progress, and how to deal with them;
▶ involving project participants. This is good practice, and a good way to involve local community members in the decision-making process. Project participants also provide a different perspective and they can be a very motivating force;
▶ providing a learning experience for all members, as ideas and different points of view are discussed;
▶ helping to embed ideas from project work in members' organisations.

Start small

In any project it is important to be realistic about what you can offer and achieve. Making promises that cannot be kept can be demoralising and can raise expectations that cannot be met. This can alienate you from your intended project participants or partners. Resources can be very stretched. Knowing what is achievable without sacrificing quality and burning-out staff or abusing their goodwill is crucial. It is also important to set yourself realistic time-lines and targets. Working with hard-to-reach learners can be slow to yield results. Being clear about this at the start, and making sure that your own management or funders know this, will prevent any negative judgements about your effectiveness. Working within health improvement and with hard-to-reach learners often involves changing long-clung-to habits, beliefs and attitudes. It may also involve changing the culture of the environment in which you are working. Start by running a pilot or taster sessions. Evaluate the effectiveness of what you are doing and make any necessary changes to your planning or provision if you need to.

Issues to take into consideration

Whether you are running this project from existing resources or writing a bid to secure funding you need to consider some of the following:

▶ This type of work can be 'time-greedy'. Working with individuals as in the 'Prescriptions for Learning' project can take time before you see any results in terms of enrolments or successful learning outcomes. Tutors working with groups in places that are not used to having learning programmes provided for them, such as in residential homes, need to be given time to set up rooms, get to know staff, or transport materials. Courses for mental health services users in colleges should allow enough time for the teaching, but also for the tutor to have a coffee break with learners. Such time can be valuable for the tutor to establish a rapport with the learners and help them get used to the environment of a learning provider, and to using its facilities.

▶ Build in time for staff briefing. Care staff, hospital staff and managers of homes and hostels may need training to raise their awareness of the health and well-being benefits of learning. Providing sessions for them may elicit their support for the work of the tutor or the learning adviser. They may be better placed to encourage residents to participate, and can make sure that other events taking place do not clash with the learning opportunity and prevent learners from attending. One tutor turned up to deliver learning in a residential home only to find that residents were going out on an outing. Tutors working in a hostel for people recovering from drug and alcohol misuse found that to get enough people to make up a group they had to knock on people's doors to get them out of bed.

▶ Build in time for training and support of tutors and learning advisers. This may be a new area of work for them, and it may throw up training and support issues. For example, do tutors know appropriate teaching and learning strategies for working with elderly and frail learners? Similarly, learning advisers who work with people on a one-to-one basis may need support to maintain professional boundaries, or to discuss the work they are doing with particular individuals.

▶ Build in time to evaluate the work that you do. This should be carried out by the tutor and preferably somebody other than the tutor, so you need to identify who will do it and how; co-evaluation with another colleague can be mutually rewarding.

▶ Good administrative support is also important. If you want to evaluate a project over a period, administrative support to set up a database to track learners from the start helps enormously. You may want to maintain contact with learners, or provide a named person or telephone contact number for learners to ring if they require help or advice. A person responsible for sending out letters, information and minutes of meetings can free up the tutor or learning adviser's time, and ensure good communication with learners and partners.

▶ Be aware of what resources are already to hand. Some learning providers or health improvement teams may already have learning materials or course outlines that they already use which, with some adaptation, could be used with your learners.

▶ If you are encouraging learners to access general learning programmes be aware of any restrictions or start dates. For example, setting up a 'Prescriptions for Learning' type project in March/April time may create difficulties if learners have to wait until September for most of the courses to start. Similarly, transport can be a key barrier in rural areas, or for people with restricted mobility.

Attention to detail

In supporting individuals to participate in learning, meticulous attention to detail is required. The slightest mishap or delay may increase anxiety, or be enough to deter somebody who is already in two minds as to whether they will cope or be accepted. Some questions to ask include the following:

▶ Is your publicity appropriate, sensitive, attractive and written in plain language? Does it provide all the information that potential learners will need to know before they decide to join the course? Does it have information about cost, childcare, times, venue, bus routes etc? Are all directions to your venue clear?

▶ Is the venue in which you will be working conducive to teaching? Is it warm, light and airy? If you are teaching in the community, will you have to compete with a television or pool table? Will learners have tables to work at, or will they have to balance things on their knees in armchairs? This can be the reality of working in some venues and you will need to bear all these factors in mind when you decide what curriculum or activity to offer.

▶ Is the curriculum content clear and appropriate? An outline of what learners can expect at each session can help. Be prepared to change or adapt the content if learners want something else included. You need to be sensitive about how you deliver the sessions. Some learners may find some activities uncomfortable; role-playing or an over-reliance on written material can be intimidating or inappropriate.

▶ Will there be somebody who can meet learners when they arrive? Tutors and session leaders need to be friendly, to approach people and include them in activities. You need to build in time for social contact, such as a coffee break, which will allow tutors to get to know people.

▶ Joint working can be very helpful as it will mean that learners can get more one-to-one time, but if you are incorporating learning about health into another activity then having somebody with expertise in that area is crucial when it comes to answering questions and providing the right information.

Partnership working

Throughout this guide, partnership working has been a key theme. Partnerships bring together organisations and groups who would not normally work together, and this provides a much more comprehensive picture of local needs. When organisations see the whole picture they can also see the gaps. Partnership working means that those gaps are more likely to be eliminated. However, partnerships also help in an operational way, because they enable organisations and groups to work with individuals holistically, addressing all their needs.

Partnerships should also involve users of services, as well as service providers. This may be difficult at the outset of a project, but users of services can be brought in at a later date. They can run the risk of being tokenistic, so it is important that all partners listen to the views of all members. Each member will have valid contributions to make and all views need to be respected or the partnership will fail.

Partnership working also increases the knowledge of the organisation and their understanding of each others' roles. Staff within organisations can sometimes fear that partnership working will lead to a blurring of roles, and that untrained people will start to do their jobs, leading to a 'dumbing down' of their work and reduced professionalism. However, what is more likely to happen is that individuals within organisations and groups gain a better appreciation of the expertise of others, which can lead to a greater defining of roles. It enables individuals to learn from each other and is more likely to lead to an 'up-skilling' of staff and members in a partnership. It also allows staff to get on with their job, and means that they don't feel they have to be all things to all people. The Project Coordinator for Walsall Community Arts project, which took health checks for men to local pubs, thought it was a great example of different disciplines uniting and building on each other's strengths. She wrote:

> 'The arts workers and health workers got on really well and complemented each other a lot. Arts workers didn't have to make any "apologies" for not having expert medical knowledge, because if participants wanted information or help they could go directly to the health workers. The health workers didn't have to "don a red nose" and break the ice with people, because participants were guided to them by the arts workers.'

Partnership working puts all members on a steep learning curve, and it can change perceptions of how services should be run and how resources should be allocated. Partnership working also allows for a more effective pooling of resources and knowledge. Effective partnership works best when:

▶ partners work together to find creative solutions. Individuals, groups or organisations can sometimes make assumptions that their values, their message or their way of working is the only way or, worse, that it is the best way. Partnership working can sometimes involve quite lengthy and, at times, difficult conversations about what needs to be done and how it can be achieved. However, by listening to each other and discussing the issues, new ways of tackling problems and new ways of working can be arrived at. Partnerships can be very creative forces;

▶ there is shared vision. By working through issues and taking on board others' ideas a shared vision can be reached. Partnership working means that there is a clear communication about what needs to change, and it avoids conflicting messages being given out. This improves credibility;

▶ clear targets and timelines are set. Reaching these can keep members of the partnership motivated, and highlights your achievements to the community and your funders;

▶ there is shared responsibility. Partnerships work best when they operate at many levels. Senior managers need to be as involved, and as understanding, of what needs to be done and how it can be achieved, as the users of the service;

▶ there is sufficient time given to it. It takes time to 'clear the ground' and to agree on what needs to be done. It also takes time to put into action the plans you have agreed on, and time to get all the partners around the table;

▶ members of the partnerships have sufficient status within their organisation or group to make or influence decisions and to release resources;

▶ where the aim is to embed successful work into the mainstream of provision. This ensures that the good work is not lost, and that the project does not become just another project that was tried and tested, and then abandoned.

Funding

Provision that is aimed at widening participation in learning and at health improvement is funded through a multiplicity of sources, and with a great deal of ingenuity. However, this does not always make it easy to get such work off the ground, and can make the development even more time-consuming.

Education funding

Most learning and health work that is carried out by learning providers is funded by short-term funding streams, such as the Adult and Community Learning Fund, Non-Schedule 2 funding, or other funding, such as from the European Social Fund or Single Regeneration Budgets. While these funding streams have given rise to many innovative projects, the work sometimes disappears when the funding ends. Sustainability can be an issue when these funding sources are used because of the geographical nature of the funding, as in SRB (Single Regeneration Budgets) funding, or because they are too short-term. Health and learning benefits can take time to show returns and, therefore, may not appear to be viable.

Some adult learning providers have used the FEFC (Further Education Funding Council) and now LSC (Learning and Skills Council) funding methodology to fund work. This has been particularly evident in the work with mental health service users that some learning providers have developed. However, until recently there were restrictions on non-accredited learning, and lack of flexibility in how providers were prepared to use funding for learning support meant that growth in provision was hampered. It is unclear at the moment what implications the new funding methodology, which will come on stream in April 2002, will have for learning providers who want to set up provision in partnership with health providers, or to improve health. Funding for Additional Support Units will remain as it is for the foreseeable future.

Fortunately, some learning providers have been creative in how they fund this area of work. Some have 'bought' in the services of their local occupational therapy teams or other healthcare professionals, to provide the support individuals might need to access learning and support while in learning. In Gloucestershire, this has led to an occupational therapist being seconded to the local college. The college has gained his expertise and contact with potential learners, and mental health services have been more able to meet the demands of care plans. This approach may find more credence with the introduction of the National Service Framework, which requires Mental Health Services to be mindful of service users' training and employment needs.

There is no clear funding stream for outreach guidance and this has also created difficulties in setting up provision that uses guidance as a strategy to widening participation in learning. Some providers have used additional support units, claimed through the funding methodology, but procedures need to be set up to show the amount of work that has been carried out with each individual and, administratively, this can generate huge amounts of paper-work. More importantly, working with individuals rather than with groups is time-consuming, despite it being a very valuable way to engage hard-to-reach learners. Many providers do not feel they can afford to invest the time and resources before they get sufficient returns. Some projects have been supported through Information, Advice and Guidance (IAG) networks. IAG managers can usually be contacted through the local careers companies.

Health funding

Until recently, funding for health improvement has often come from joint finance. Health Authorities and Local Authorities have dispensed monies through Primary Care Groups or Primary Care Trust via HimPs funding. Health services are going through major changes at the moment, with Health Authorities being devolved into Strategic Health Authorities. At the time of writing, the future of funding for health improvement is unclear, although it is clear that health improvement funds will be devolved to Primary Care Teams. These will have a developmental role for health improvement and for delivering public health. There are likely to be targets to achieve for public health improvement, which are still under consultation. Primary Care Teams may be able to ring-fence some monies for health improvement projects. Partnerships between learning providers, voluntary sector and community groups, for example, might find themselves in a position to influence Primary Care Teams in how they might attain these health inequality targets. GP practices may wish to develop their own projects around learning and health. In theory, they should be able to build such ideas into their practice development plans and bid for development money to the Primary Care Trust. Primary care funding could therefore be used to support any development work led by GP practices.

Local Strategic Partnerships are also in the process of being set up. While they may make joint bids for funding, or bring agencies together to joint fund work, they do not have a designated source of funding.

From April 2001, health and local authorities have been required to complete a Joint Investment Plan. JIPs are three-year rolling programmes aimed at supporting delivery of key aspects of HImPs. The Department of Health states that:

> 'Joint investment planning may well be the catalyst for developing arrangements that would benefit from the use of lead commissioning, integrated provision and pooled budgets.'[2]

JIPs could therefore become an important source of information and support for partnership work and funding.

Health Action Zones have, in recent years, been a useful source of funding for integrated approaches to health improvement. From March 2002, Health Action Zones will cease to exist in their current form, how they will be continued is still under discussion.

Funding sustainable learning and health work

Learning that promotes health improvement is often cross-sectoral and, as such, funding is often an issue. Minter illustrates the point well:

> '...should there be a holistic approach to older people's needs that should be matched funded across education, health and social services? We fund an organisation in RBKC (Royal Borough of Kensington and Chelsea) that is an Open Age project that offers a broad range of activities across learning, health and social events for older people over 50. Is this the sort of approach that other groups might take and what would be the implications for funding?"

Family learning, because it is inter-generational and cross-sectoral, shares many of the issues and difficulties involved with funding and sustainability as provision that improves health through learning. In 'A Manifesto for Family Learning' there is a call for a:

'long-term funding framework, which supports cross-sectoral partnership work for a broad range of integrated FL activities'.[3]

Such a funding framework in learning and health would enable major development in this area of work.

Summary

This chapter has given some practical suggestions for setting up projects that promote health improvement through learning, and emphasises the time and attention to detail that is required if the planned work is going to be effective. The chapter also emphasises the benefits of partnership working, and, crucially, the importance and benefits of learner involvement. However, working in this way can create challenges for the way that projects are managed and funded, both of which are key to the future development of this area of work.

References

1   McGivney, V. (2000). *Recovering outreach*, NIACE.
2   Department of Health (25th October 2001). *Department of Health Guidance on Joint Investment Plans*, www.doh.gov.uk/jointunit/jipguidance/htm.
3   Haggart, J. (2000). *Learning Legacies. A Guide to Family Learning*, NIACE.

South Downs NHS Trust, Health Promotion, Age Concern,
Community Leisure 'Add Life' Health Improvement Course

8

Quality, evaluation and dissemination

This chapter looks at quality, evaluation and dissemination. Once your project is up and running, the quality of what you do will affect your success. But, unless you can show your effectiveness, all your good work will remained uncelebrated. Once you know what works and why it is successful, you need to celebrate it and make sure that as many people as possible know about it. You therefore need to disseminate your findings.

Even if your project does not turn out as expected, it will be important to know why and learn from it. Disseminating that information could also prevent other people for making the same mistakes as you.

Quality

Once a programme of learning and health is underway you will want to ensure that the quality of the provision is good. Quality assurance ensures greater accountability for learners and funders. As provision aimed at health improvement through learning often involves cross-sectoral collaboration, it does not sit within one framework for quality assurance. Each agency, be it health services, learning provider, leisure services or Local Authority, will have its own quality indicators. Sometimes these can seem needlessly bureaucratic or burdensome, especially for a small project. However, community or outreach work can often be perceived to be marginal, so ensuring that use of the same quality indicators will give your work a rigour that can increase its credibility. You will need to use your judgement as to how you incorporate quality assurance into your work. However, there are some issues about the interface of cross-sectoral working that you might want to consider to ensure the quality of your work.

▶ Terminology. Each service has its own language and way of describing things. For example, health services refer to users of their services as 'patients'; learning providers use the words 'student' or 'learner', and guidance services use the word 'client'. Agreeing on and using the right terminology in the right context is important. For example, learners referred by health services and working in small groups within a learning environment, should not be referred to as 'patients'. To do so immediately sets them apart. Importantly for long-term users of health services, being known as 'students' or 'learners' represents a move forward and allows individuals to assume a new identity.

▶ Confidentiality. Health staff, workers in social services, housing associations and care homes will invariably know a great deal about an individual's private life. Tutors and learning advisers may feel that they need to know something about the learners before they work with them. Asking yourself: 'How will this person's health or situation affect their learning?' is the best way to think about this issue. You will need to agree on what information is exchanged. Group participants will need to be informed as to what information is being exchanged, or encouraged to decide for themselves what a tutor might need to know about them. Encouraging learners to do this for themselves gets them to start thinking about their learning needs, but also about what their strengths are.

One college gave students with mental health needs the opportunity to think through their learning needs and to write a letter to their tutor about what they thought these were. When students thought this through, all that they usually needed to tell their tutor were simple things such as that they would be really nervous when they started at college, and this would affect their concentration, or that their medication made them thirsty so they would need to bring a drink into class. Similarly, one residential home that provided learning programmes for its residents decided to ask the residents what they wanted the tutor to know about them. Care staff found out more about what the residents had done in their younger days than they had ever known, and saw residents in a new light from then on.

Talking about your learning and what works for you makes you a learner or student, rather than a patient, client or service user. Being clear and transparent about information is good practice, and getting the right background information on learners also assists the tutor on delivering good teaching.

► Boundaries. Working in a health and learning situation will mean that sometimes there can be a blurring of roles. This is especially so when a member of staff, such as a learning adviser, could be working with individuals on a one-to-one basis. The learning adviser in the NIACE project in Nottingham has a mentor/supervisor with whom he meets regularly to discuss particular aspects of his work with some individuals. This ensures that he has some support for his own emotional well-being. It also enables him to be clear with the people who he is working with about his remit, and what he can and cannot help with. In certain situations he refers individuals to other agencies for support with some aspect of their life. Supervision for counsellors is part of the accepted way of working. Supervision for learning advisers and for those working with mental health service users is equally important.

► Risk assessment. In some project, particularly guidance focussed activities, it may become apparent that the individual has behaviours that might present a risk to themselves or others. This does not happen often, but where it does, it is important that this does not become a barrier to their learning, and that it is dealt with in a way that is respectful to the individual, as well as to other learners and to staff. Some colleges have now drawn up procedures to help them work positively and clearly with individuals and referring agencies, so that individuals are enabled to learn in an environment that does not exacerbate any risk behaviour. For example, risk assessment and behaviour support plans have been used very effectively at New College Nottingham to support learners with mental health needs and young people with challenging behaviour.

▶ User involvement. As already mentioned, involving users in the decision-making process can be beneficial to the project, and it also ensures that you are meeting their needs. As one learner who was involved in a steering group said:

> 'It felt really good when they (the college) acted upon the ideas we had for improving things. The improvements were small but they helped, but mostly we all felt listened to.'

Evaluation

When you evaluate your work you will need to evaluate the learning outcomes and health improvement outcomes of your work. In the setting-up phase of your project you will have decided whether there are any specific learning outcomes or health improvement outcomes that you specifically want to measure. Being clear at the start of the project as to what outcomes should be measured is crucial. You may also be required to show the cost-effectiveness of your work, particularly if there is an issue of further funding and sustainability.

Learning provision that aims to promote health is often carried out in community settings and can be seen to be expensive. Such work is often carried out with the most disadvantaged groups, so tutors may work with smaller groups, or guidance workers may need more than one guidance interview to help somebody overcome their anxieties about learning. However, the alternative of somebody remaining on anti-depressants, or of continuing to smoke, or of remaining on benefit, or going off on long-term sick leave, will be much more expensive. The problem is that it is very hard to prove the longer-term cost benefits. How do you prove that they wouldn't have come off medication, or given up smoking or found a job anyway? Equally, in the area of learning and health, proving effectiveness is also complicated by the fact that the cost of such work might be incurred by a learning provider, but the benefits might be accrued by health services. The improved sense of well-being of adults might have the greatest benefits for their children and, therefore, may take years to bear fruit.

Evaluation of the work that you do is very important and you need to think carefully about what you want to evaluate. Effective evaluation will have an impact on the chances of the work being sustained and who is likely to sustain it. It is also a mark of effective teaching and learning to seek to learn from the work that you do.

Like quality, the evaluation of learning and health programmes does not fit into a neat common framework. The various agencies, who are all players in the arena of learning and health, will have their own evaluation framework. However, if your project is funded from another source, you are often required to show how you will evaluate your work within your bid. One thing is certain in deciding how you evaluate your work, collecting evidence as you go along is a lot easier than trying to do it at the end. Evaluating your work as you progress is particularly helpful if your project is long-term; you can see how the work is progressing and whether you need to make any changes along the way.

The type of quantitative data that you might want to collect could be:

▶ information on project participants, such as gender, age, ethnicity, address, previous learning;

▶ information about participants' health before the project, such as weight, blood pressure, muscle strength, medication use, attendance and use of health resources;

▶ comparable information on participants' health after the project;

▶ health behaviours before and after the project, such as exercise taken, alcohol consumption or smoking habits;

▶ take-up of preventative services before and after the project;

▶ attendance at sessions, learning programmes, guidance interviews or activities;

▶ participation in learning before and after the project, including types of learning, any accredited learning outcomes and any progression.

Qualitative evidence can be a rich source of information, and enables you to capture the voices of project participants, tutors and healthcare staff. This can provide different perspectives on the outcomes of your work. Qualitative evidence could be:

▶ outlines of the activities that people attended, with details of learning programmes, guidance interviews conducted, sessions attended, or exercise activities;

▶ the learners' views on the sessions, what they found helpful or useful, or what they didn't like and what they felt they learned;

▶ learners' perceptions about their health before and after the project, and what evidence they have for making these statements;

▶ wider benefits of the project, for example, new friendships, being more assertive, other health behaviours, or other health benefits—such as improved sleeping;

▶ the views of all staff involved in the project or within the organisation you are in partnership with. For example, the effect on their role and their perception of the health benefits to learners;

▶ other outcomes, such as the effectiveness of partnerships formed and lessons learned. Recording other offshoots and unexpected outcomes of your project and other work developed can also be valuable.

While we have separate sectors of education, health, leisure, social services etc., with their separate funding and targets, partnership working will always be a conscious effort, it will never become the norm.

Dissemination

Once the project is finished and you have completed your evaluation you may be required to write a project report. It is usual for this report to be sent to the project funders and even to members of your steering group or partnership board. However, you might want to think about disseminating your findings further in order to:

▶ celebrate your successes and the successes of the learners;
▶ enable other people to learn from your good practice;
▶ inform and influence policy makers and managers.

Dissemination can be done in many ways and it is always more powerful when it reflects the learners' views and comments. Some tips include:

▶ sending your report, or shortened version, to individuals who may have an interest;
▶ giving talks or presenting workshops at conferences;
▶ posting your report on a website;
▶ writing articles for journals. *Adults Learning*, NIACE's in-house journal, welcomes articles on good practice. Health services and local authorities may have their own newsletter and editors are often looking for good material;
▶ putting together a press release and sending to local and national newspaper and radio stations can also elicit positive responses. 'Big Bites for *Big Issue* Vendors' and 'Prescriptions for Learning' have both been featured on the radio and in the press;

▶ enter your good work for awards, such as Adult Learners' Week and other learning and health sector awards.

Summary

Ensuring the quality of the work that you do is a key issue. Evaluation will enable you to show the effectiveness of your work in promoting health improvement and learning. It will also enable you to show how you achieved your outcomes. Involving learners in evaluation in ways that draw on their experience, and involving them in dissemination, can be very positive for staff and learners.

Part 4

What next?

Moving forward

This book has provided a brief overview of learning approaches for improved health. There is a diverse range of provision and a variety of approaches. There is learning for prevention of ill-health and learning for rehabilitation, as well as learning for personal development and fulfilment of potential. There is also individual and community learning.

This chapter identifies areas of understanding that need to be explored further and suggests measures that could be taken to reduce the barriers that are hampering the developments of learning and approaches to health. This chapter looks at where we need to go next.

Walsall Community Arts Project

9

The current picture

A wealth of provision addresses the health and learning needs of individuals and communities. Those mentioned in this book are but a few. Practitioners in health services, education services, leisure services, voluntary and other services have shown great imagination and innovation in approaching health improvement through learning, and emerging findings have been positive and informative. This is an exciting and dynamic area of work.

The overall picture of developments is one of diversity and variety. Bringing all the approaches and strategy together has been akin to stitching a patchwork quilt of many different colours and textures, rather than presenting the uniform coverage of a blanket.

The learner's voice throughout the provision has been strong, and has provided a perspective that has been thought provoking and added a different dimension. In talking to learners and reading their stories it is apparent that the impact which participation in these projects and in learning had on their lives is significant and far-reaching. However, we cannot afford to be complacent.

Looking forward

There is still too much to do and too much at stake. Projects have shown that, if people are engaged in learning about their health, they often move on to other learning opportunities. Equally, when people have engaged in learning, they have often experienced health benefits and improved health behaviours. These are important and valuable outcomes but, within the current mainstream funding, do not meet the right targets. They do not result, at least in the short term, in qualifications or reductions in appointment waiting times. A joint funding framework is required that allows for diversity of provision, a variety of outcomes, and recognises that progression routes for adults are a reflection of the complexity of individual needs. A funding framework that recognises the 'whole-person' needs of learners is essential.

A joint funding framework would allow for greater development of cross-sector working. Primary Care Teams are multi-disciplinary across health and social-care professions, but initiatives to include education, leisure, or voluntary staff within the team encounter difficulties with funding. Until a way is found to fund cross-sector working, we will always struggle with basing learning advisers in surgeries, nurses in learning provision, or having practitioners from different sectors working alongside each other as a matter of course. Until a way of funding cross-sector work is found, initiatives that address the learning and health needs of individuals and communities are likely to remain short-term and precarious. Sustainability of good practice will therefore always be an issue.

The development of a joint funding framework would also facilitate more meaningful and sustained partnership working. Without adequate time and resources, partnerships across sectors can be transient and superficial, and lacking in any real shared understanding and appreciation of the role each partner has to play. While there are still separate funding streams, there will remain a preciousness about resources that does not encourage practitioners to raise their heads above the parapets of their own organisations. An atmosphere of greater openness, facilitated through joint funding, would encourage practitioners to recognise the value in learning from each other, and the value of their own contribution. There is still much to be learnt about truly effective partnership working, which needs to start with the initial training of practitioners and to be part of continuing professional development. Effective partnership working adds value to the partner organisations and to the joint work they do. Understanding what makes partnerships effective and successful, and how practitioners who work cross-sector and in partnership can be supported, is crucial.

Guidance has been an essential element in some of the projects and greater clarification as to the role of guidance is important. Guidance, when used effectively, can enable individuals to make sense of the learning journey they need to embark on in order to make the changes they want to make in their lives. However, because guidance is person-centred and addresses the needs of the whole person, funders and managers can be wary of an approach that appears to be intensive and time-greedy. More work in highlighting good practice that supports lifelong learning and improved health, but which also engenders independence in decision-making and motivation among individuals is required.

Underpinning much of the work within these learning and health projects has been the recognition that raised self-esteem has been an important outcome experienced by many learners. Poor self-esteem is often reported to be the biggest barrier to making a change in an individual's life, whether it is to access learning, to be more active in the community, or to adopt a healthier lifestyle. Yet low self-esteem may also be the barrier that prevents individuals from seeking support to make whatever change they want to bring about in their lives. GP surgeries can often be the first, or frequent, point of contact for people when their situation becomes increasingly intolerable to them. Understanding what strategies and approaches are necessary to support GPs and healthcare staff in raising individual's self-esteem is another important area for further work.

Finally, there is a need and an urgency to add more pieces to this growing patchwork of different colours and textures. All the various projects, initiatives and approaches that seek to improve health through learning need to be identified. There are other connections to be made, particularly among projects about conservation, environment and food production, which have not featured in this book but are nevertheless areas where exciting work is being done. We do not have time to constantly re-invent the wheel. There are important stories to be told and lessons to be learned from them all. All of the provision linking learning to health improvement indicates this is a rich seam that promises to yield exciting and 'joined-up' learning opportunities, which will be challenging and thought provoking.